1994
YEARBOOK of
ASTRONOMY

1994 YEARBOOK of ASTRONOMY

edited by
Patrick Moore

Sidgwick & Jackson Limited
LONDON

First Published 1993 by Sidgwick & Jackson Limited
a division of Pan Macmillan Publishers Limited
Cavaye Place London SW10 9PG
and Basingstoke

Associated companies throughout the world

ISBN 0–283–06138–3 (hardback)
0–283–06139–1 (paperback)

1 2 3 4 5 6 7 8 9

*A CIP catalogue record for this book is available from
the British Library*

*Photoset by Rowland Phototypesetting Limited
Bury St Edmunds, Suffolk
Printed and bound in Great Britain by
Mackays of Chatham PLC, Chatham, Kent*

Contents

Part II: *Article Section*

Part III: *Miscellaneous*

Editor's Foreword

There are no major changes in the format or arrangement of the latest *Yearbook*. As usual, Gordon Taylor has provided the monthly charts and data, and we have contributions from our regular authors, notably Dr David Allen, who has been such a pillar of strength of the *Yearbook* over the years. Dr Peter Cattermole deals with the latest Venus research, and Dr David Jewitt takes us out to the frontiers of the planetary system; Dr Ian McLean introduces us to the latest infrared research, Donald Trombino deals with the Sun, and Dr Allan Chapman with some fascinating history. We also welcome Leif Robinson, Editor of *Sky and Telescope*, with his timely and thought-provoking article. Thanks too to John Isles, our variable star expert, and to Bill Procter for all his organizational help.

PATRICK MOORE
Selsey, May 1993

Preface

New readers will find that all the information in this *Yearbook* is given in diagrammatic or descriptive form; the positions of the planets may easily be found on the specially designed star charts, while the monthly notes describe the movements of the planets and give details of other astronomical phenomena visible in both the northern and southern hemispheres. Two sets of the star charts are provided. The **Northern Charts** (pp. 14 to 39) are designed for use in latitude 52 degrees north, but may be used without alteration throughout the British Isles, and (except in the case of eclipses and occultations) in other countries of similar north latitude. The **Southern Charts** (pp. 40 to 65) are drawn for latitude 35 degrees south, and are suitable for use in South Africa, Australia and New Zealand, and other stations in approximately the same south latitude. The reader who needs more detailed information will find *Norton's Star Atlas* (Longman) an invaluable guide, while more precise positions of the planets and their satellites, together with predictions of occultations, meteor showers, and periodic comets may be found in the *Handbook* of the British Astronomical Association. The British monthly periodical, with current news, articles, and monthly notes is *Astronomy Now*. Readers will also find details of forthcoming events given in the American *Sky and Telescope*. This monthly publication also produces a special occultation supplement giving predictions for the United States and Canada.

Important Note
The times given on the star charts and in the Monthly Notes are generally given as local times, using the 24-hour clock, the day beginning at midnight. All the dates, and the times of a few events (e.g. eclipses), are given in Greenwich Mean Time (G.M.T.), which is related to local time by the formula

Local Mean Time = G.M.T. − west longitude

In practice, small differences of longitudes are ignored, and the observer will use local clock time, which will be the appropriate

Standard (or Zone) Time. As the formula indicates, places in west longitude will have a Standard Time slow on G.M.T., while places in east longitude will have a Standard Time fast on G.M.T. As examples we have:

Standard Time in

New Zealand	G.M.T.	+	12 hours
Victoria; N.S.W.	G.M.T.	+	10 hours
Western Australia	G.M.T.	+	8 hours
South Africa	G.M.T.	+	2 hours
British Isles	G.M.T.		
Eastern S.T.	G.M.T.	−	5 hours
Central S.T.	G.M.T.	−	6 hours, etc.

If Summer Time is in use, the clocks will have to have been advanced by one hour, and this hour must be subtracted from the clock time to give Standard Time.

In Great Britain and N. Ireland, Summer Time will be in force in 1994 from March 27^{d}01^h until October 23^{d}01^h G.M.T.

Notes on the Star Charts

The stars, together with the Sun, Moon and planets seem to be set on the surface of the celestial sphere, which appears to rotate about the Earth from east to west. Since it is impossible to represent a curved surface accurately on a plane, any kind of star map is bound to contain some form of distortion. But it is well known that the eye can endure some kinds of distortion better than others, and it is particularly true that the eye is most sensitive to deviations from the vertical and horizontal. For this reason the star charts given in this volume have been designed to give a true representation of vertical and horizontal lines, whatever may be the resulting distortion in the shape of a constellation figure. It will be found that the amount of distortion is, in general, quite small, and is only obvious in the case of large constellations such as Leo and Pegasus, when these appear at the top of the charts, and so are drawn out sideways.

The charts show all stars down to the fourth magnitude, together with a number of fainter stars which are necessary to define the shape of a constellation. There is no standard system for representing the outlines of the constellations, and triangles and other simple figures have been used to give outlines which are easy to follow with the naked eye. The names of the constellations are given, together with the proper names of the brighter stars. The apparent magnitudes of the stars are indicated roughly by using four different sizes of dots, the larger dots representing the brighter stars.

The two sets of star charts are similar in design. At each opening there is a group of four charts which give a complete coverage of the sky up to an altitude of 62½ degrees; there are twelve such groups to cover the entire year. In the **Northern Charts** (for 52 degrees north) the upper two charts show the southern sky, south being at the centre and east on the left. The coverage is from 10 degrees north of east (top left) to 10 degrees north of west (top right). The two lower charts show the northern sky from 10 degrees south of west (lower left) to 10 degrees south of east (lower right). There is thus an overlap east and west.

Conversely, in the **Southern Charts** (for 35 degrees south) the upper two charts show the northern sky, with north at the centre and east on the right. The two lower charts show the southern sky, with south at the centre and east on the left. The coverage and overlap is the same on both sets of charts.

Because the sidereal day is shorter than the solar day, the stars appear to rise and set about four minutes earlier each day, and this amounts to two hours in a month. Hence the twelve groups of charts in each set are sufficient to give the appearance of the sky throughout the day at intervals of two hours, or at the same time of night at monthly intervals throughout the year. The actual range of dates and times when the stars on the charts are visible is indicated at the top of each page. Each group is numbered in bold type, and the number to be used for any given month and time is summarized in the following table:

Local Time	18h	20h	22h	0h	2h	4h	6h
January	11	12	1	2	3	4	5
February	12	1	2	3	4	5	6
March	1	2	3	4	5	6	7
April	2	3	4	5	6	7	8
May	3	4	5	6	7	8	9
June	4	5	6	7	8	9	10
July	5	6	7	8	9	10	11
August	6	7	8	9	10	11	12
September	7	8	9	10	11	12	1
October	8	9	10	11	12	1	2
November	9	10	11	12	1	2	3
December	10	11	12	1	2	3	4

The charts are drawn to scale, the horizontal measurements, marked at every 10 degrees, giving the azimuths (or true bearings) measured from the north round through east (90 degrees), south (180 degrees), and west (270 degrees). The vertical measurements, similarly marked, give the altitudes of the stars up to 62½ degrees. Estimates of altitude and azimuth made from these charts will necessarily be mere approximations, since no observer will be exactly at the adopted latitude, or at the stated time, but they will serve for the identification of stars and planets.

The ecliptic is drawn as a broken line on which longitude is marked at every 10 degrees; the positions of the planets are then easily found by reference to the table on page 71. It will be noticed that on the Southern Charts the **ecliptic** may reach an altitude in excess of 62½ degrees on star charts 5 to 9. The continuations of the broken line will be found on the charts of overhead stars.

There is a curious illusion that stars at an altitude of 60 degrees or more are actually overhead, and the beginner may often feel that he is leaning over backwards in trying to see them. These overhead stars are given separately on the pages immediately following the main star charts. The entire year is covered at one opening, each of the four maps showing the overhead stars at times which correspond to those of three of the main star charts. The position of the zenith is indicated by a cross, and this cross marks the centre of a circle which is 35 degrees from the zenith; there is thus a small overlap with the main charts.

The broken line leading from the north (on the Northern Charts) or from the south (on the Southern Charts) is numbered to indicate the corresponding main chart. Thus on page 38 the N-S line numbered 6 is to be regarded as an extension of the centre (south) line of chart 6 on pages 24 and 25, and at the top of these pages are printed the dates and times which are appropriate. Similarly, on page 65, the S-N line numbered 10 connects with the north line of the upper charts on pages 58 and 59.

The overhead stars are plotted as maps on a conical projection, and the scale is rather smaller than that of the main charts.

1L

October 6 at 5^h	October 21 at 4^h
November 6 at 3^h	November 21 at 2^h
December 6 at 1^h	December 21 at midnight
January 6 at 23^h	January 21 at 22^h
February 6 at 21^h	February 21 at 20^h

October 6 at 5ʰ   October 21 at   4ʰ
November 6 at 3ʰ   November 21 at   2ʰ
December 6 at 1ʰ   December 21 at midnight
January 6 at 23ʰ   January 21 at   22ʰ
February 6 at 21ʰ February 21 at   20ʰ

1R

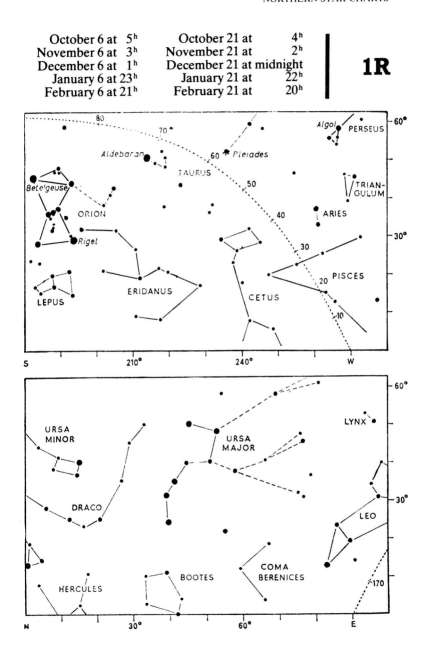

15

2L

November 6 at 5ʰ	November 21 at 4ʰ
December 6 at 3ʰ	December 21 at 2ʰ
January 6 at 1ʰ	January 21 at midnight
February 6 at 23ʰ	February 21 at 22ʰ
March 6 at 21ʰ	March 21 at 20ʰ

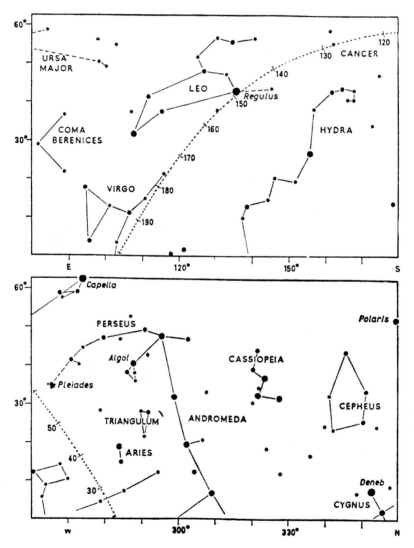

November 6 at 5ʰ November 21 at 4ʰ
December 6 at 3ʰ December 21 at 2ʰ
January 6 at 1ʰ January 21 at midnight
February 6 at 23ʰ February 21 at 22ʰ
March 6 at 21ʰ March 21 at 20ʰ

2R

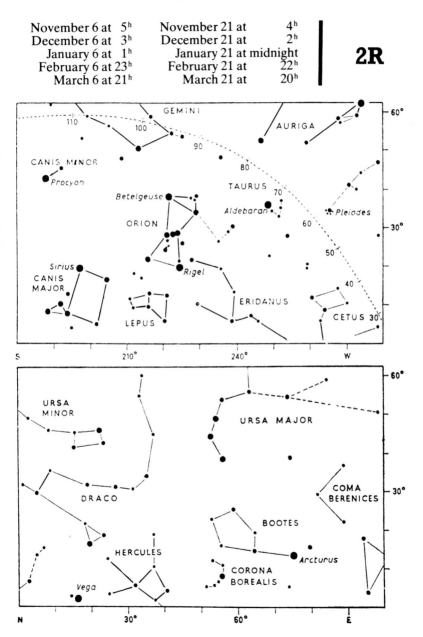

3L

December 6 at 5ʰ   December 21 at   4ʰ
January 6 at 3ʰ   January 21 at   2ʰ
February 6 at 1ʰ   February 21 at midnight
March 6 at 23ʰ   March 21 at   22ʰ
April 6 at 21ʰ   April 21 at   20ʰ

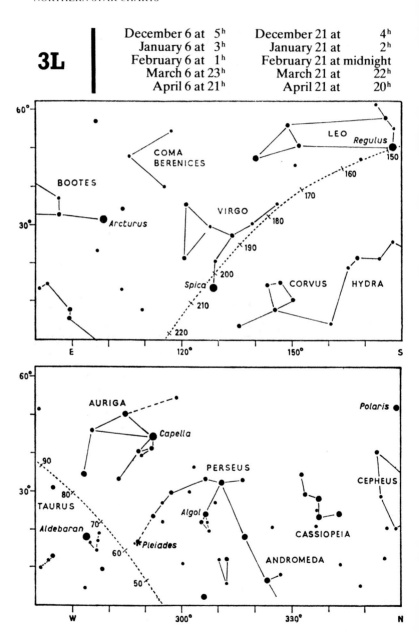

December 6 at 5^h	December 21 at 4^h
January 6 at 3^h	January 21 at 2^h
February 6 at 1^h	February 21 at midnight
March 6 at 23^h	March 21 at 22^h
April 6 at 21^h	April 21 at 20^h

3R

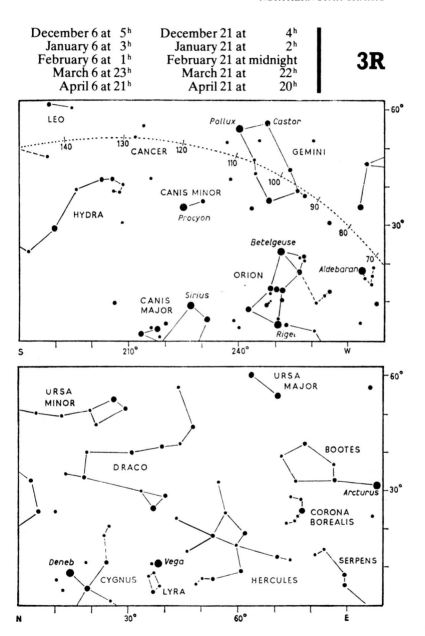

19

4L

January 6 at 5^h	January 21 at 4^h
February 6 at 3^h	February 21 at 2^h
March 6 at 1^h	March 21 at midnight
April 6 at 23^h	April 21 at 22^h
May 6 at 21^h	May 21 at 20^h

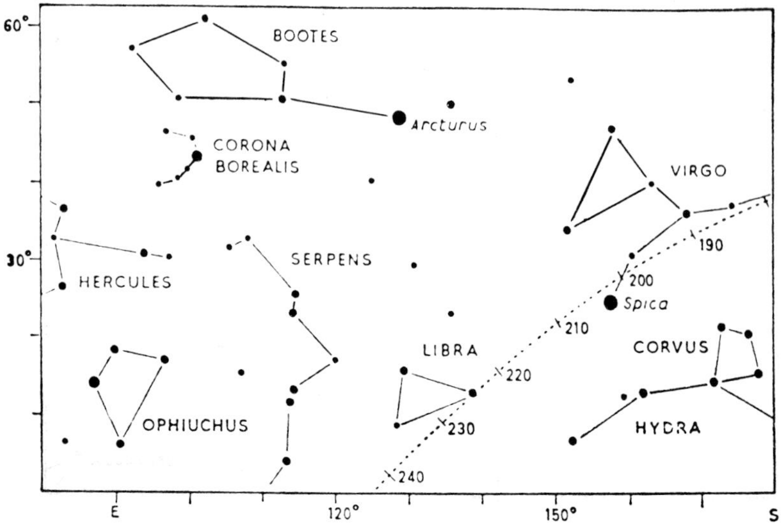

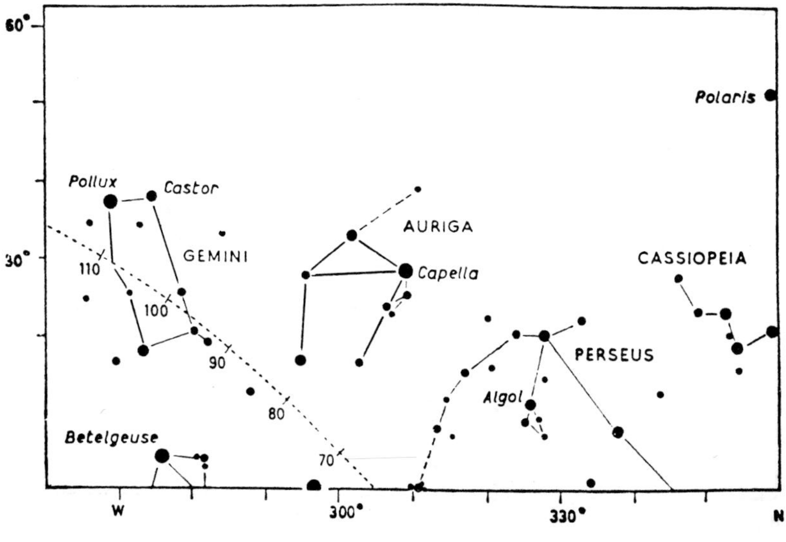

BOOTES

Arcturus

CORONA BOREALIS

VIRGO

190

200

SERPENS

Spica

210

HERCULES

LIBRA

220

CORVUS

230

OPHIUCHUS

HYDRA

240

E   120°   150°   S

Polaris

Pollux   Castor

GEMINI

AURIGA

CASSIOPEIA

110

Capella

100

90

PERSEUS

80

Algol

70

Betelgeuse

W   300°   330°   N

January 6 at 5ʰ   January 21 at   4ʰ
February 6 at 3ʰ   February 21 at   2ʰ
March 6 at 1ʰ   March 21 at midnight
April 6 at 23ʰ   April 21 at   22ʰ
May 6 at 21ʰ   May 21 at   20ʰ

4R

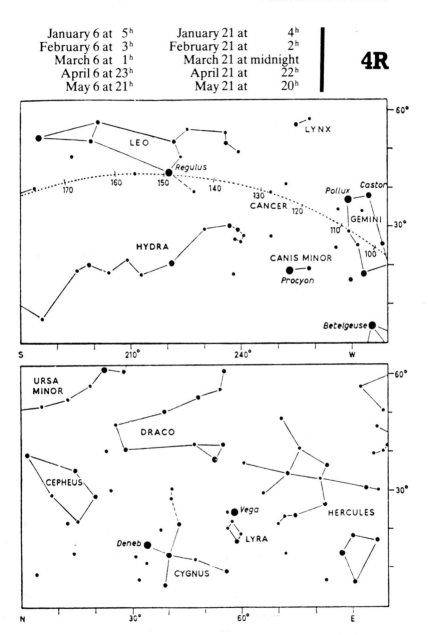

5L

January 6 at 7ʰ
February 6 at 5ʰ
March 6 at 3ʰ
April 6 at 1ʰ
May 6 at 23ʰ

January 21 at 6ʰ
February 21 at 4ʰ
March 21 at 2ʰ
April 21 at midnight
May 21 at 22ʰ

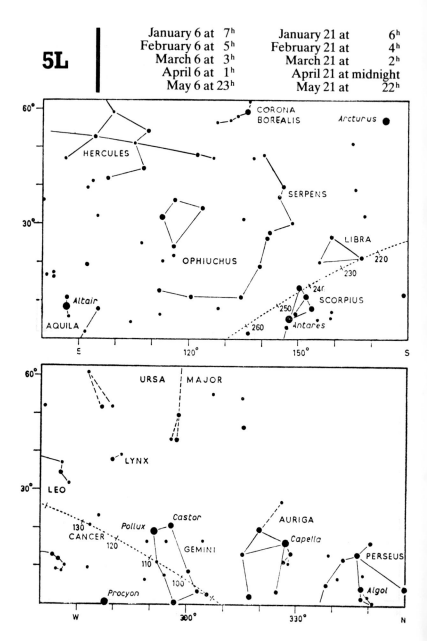

January 6 at 7ʰ	January 21 at 6ʰ
February 6 at 5ʰ	February 21 at 4ʰ
March 6 at 3ʰ	March 21 at 2ʰ
April 6 at 1ʰ	April 21 at midnight
May 6 at 23ʰ	May 21 at 22ʰ

5R

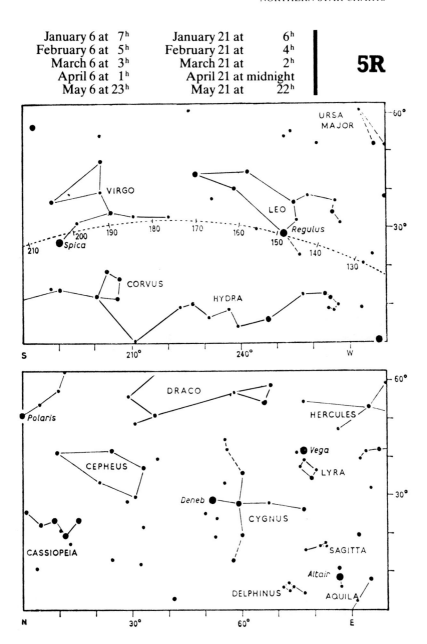

6L

March 6 at 5ʰ	March 21 at 4ʰ
April 6 at 3ʰ	April 21 at 2ʰ
May 6 at 1ʰ	May 21 at midnight
June 6 at 23ʰ	June 21 at 22ʰ
July 6 at 21ʰ	July 21 at 20ʰ

March 6 at 5ʰ   March 21 at   4ʰ
April 6 at 3ʰ   April 21 at   2ʰ
May 6 at 1ʰ   May 21 at midnight
June 6 at 23ʰ   June 21 at   22ʰ
July 6 at 21ʰ   July 21 at   20ʰ

6R

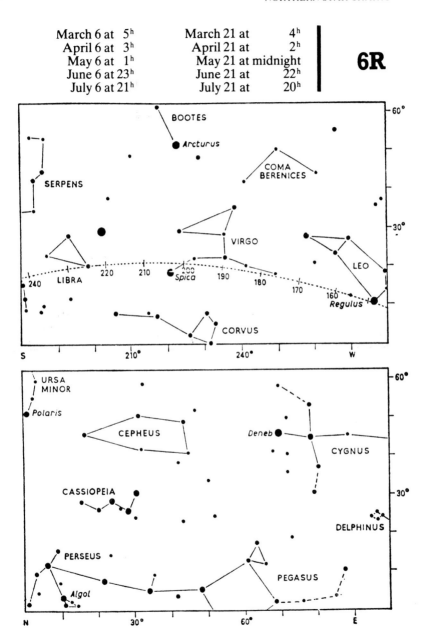

7L

May 6 at 3ʰ	May 21 at 2ʰ
June 6 at 1ʰ	June 21 at midnight
July 6 at 23ʰ	July 21 at 22ʰ
August 6 at 21ʰ	August 21 at 20ʰ
September 6 at 19ʰ	September 21 at 18ʰ

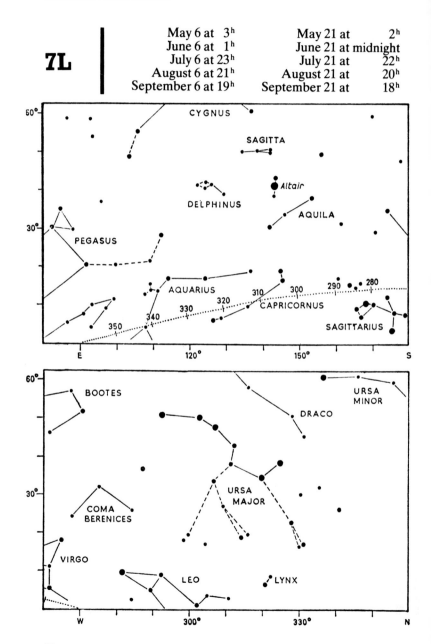

May 6 at 3ʰ
June 6 at 1ʰ
July 6 at 23ʰ
August 6 at 21ʰ
September 6 at 19ʰ

May 21 at   2ʰ
June 21 at midnight
July 21 at   22ʰ
August 21 at 20ʰ
September 21 at 18ʰ

7R

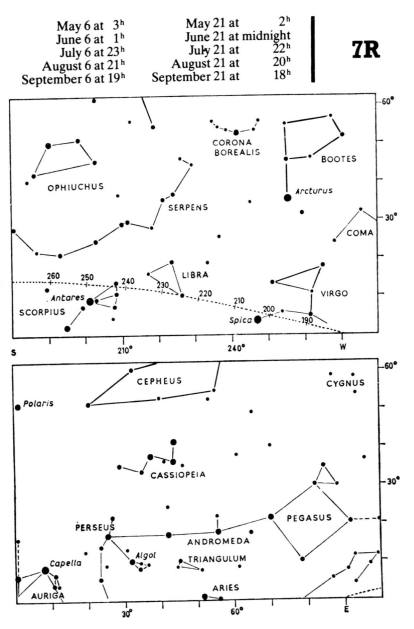

8L

July 6 at 1ʰ	July 21 at midnight
August 6 at 23ʰ	August 21 at 22ʰ
September 6 at 21ʰ	September 21 at 20ʰ
October 6 at 19ʰ	October 21 at 18ʰ
November 6 at 17ʰ	November 21 at 16ʰ

July 6 at 1ʰ   July 21 at midnight
August 6 at 23ʰ   August 21 at   22ʰ
September 6 at 21ʰ   September 21 at   20ʰ
October 6 at 19ʰ   October 21 at   18ʰ
November 6 at 17ʰ   November 21 at   16ʰ

8R

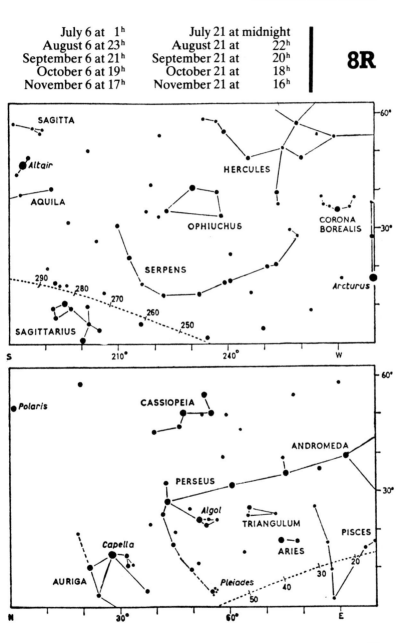

29

9L

August 6 at 1ʰ	August 21 at midnight
September 6 at 23ʰ	September 21 at 22ʰ
October 6 at 21ʰ	October 21 at 20ʰ
November 6 at 19ʰ	November 21 at 18ʰ
December 6 at 17ʰ	December 21 at 16ʰ

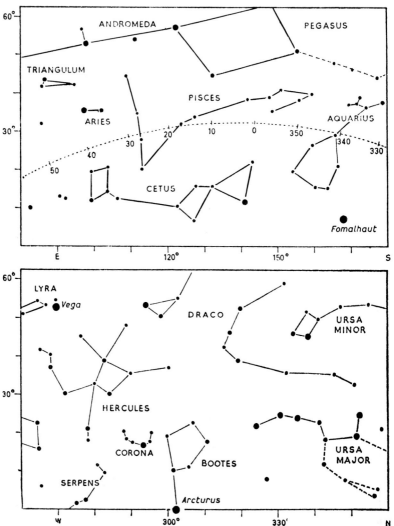

August 6 at 1ʰ	August 21 at midnight	
September 6 at 23ʰ	September 21 at 22ʰ	
October 6 at 21ʰ	October 21 at 20ʰ	**9R**
November 6 at 19ʰ	November 21 at 18ʰ	
December 6 at 17ʰ	December 21 at 16ʰ	

10L	August 6 at 3ʰ August 21 at 2ʰ September 6 at 1ʰ September 21 at midnight October 6 at 23ʰ October 21 at 22ʰ November 6 at 21ʰ November 21 at 20ʰ December 6 at 19ʰ December 21 at 18ʰ

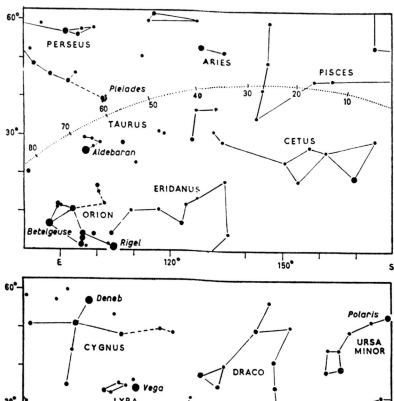

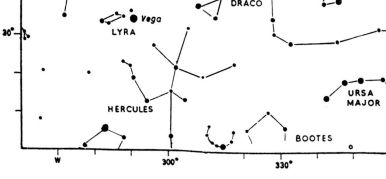

August 6 at 3ʰ	August 21 at 2ʰ	
September 6 at 1ʰ	September 21 at midnight	
October 6 at 23ʰ	October 21 at 22ʰ	**10R**
November 6 at 21ʰ	November 21 at 20ʰ	
December 6 at 19ʰ	December 21 at 18ʰ	

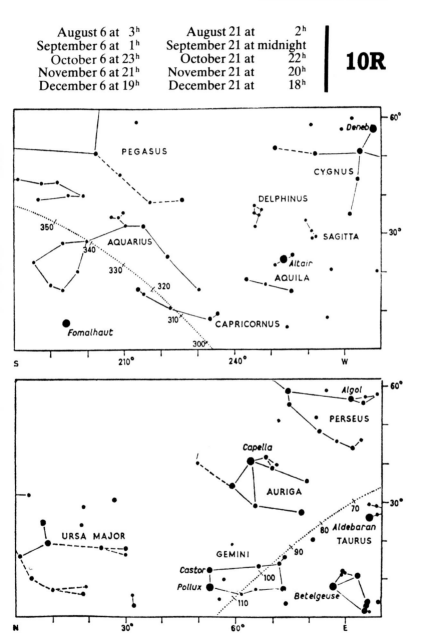

11L

September 6 at 3ʰ	September 21 at 2ʰ
October 6 at 1ʰ	October 21 at midnight
November 6 at 23ʰ	November 21 at 22ʰ
December 6 at 21ʰ	December 21 at 20ʰ
January 6 at 19ʰ	January 21 at 18ʰ

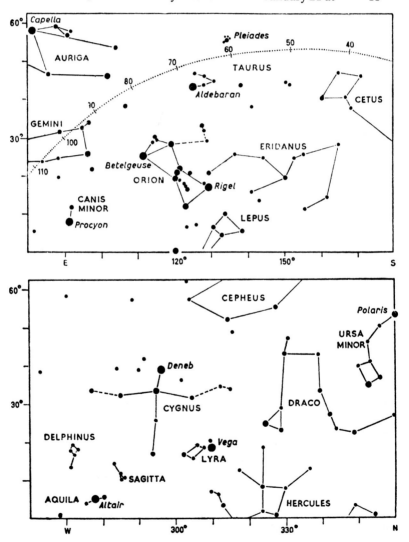

September 6 at 3ʰ	September 21 at 2ʰ	
October 6 at 1ʰ	October 21 at midnight	
November 6 at 23ʰ	November 21 at 22ʰ	**11R**
December 6 at 21ʰ	December 21 at 20ʰ	
January 6 at 19ʰ	January 21 at 18ʰ	

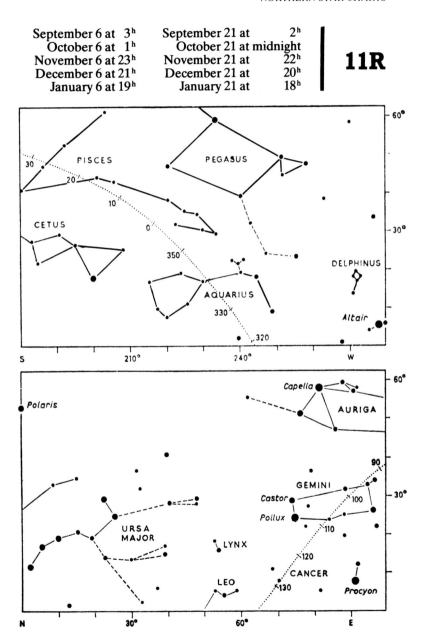

12L

October 6 at 3ʰ	October 21 at 2ʰ
November 6 at 1ʰ	November 21 at midnight
December 6 at 23ʰ	December 21 at 22ʰ
January 6 at 21ʰ	January 21 at 20ʰ
February 6 at 19ʰ	February 21 at 18ʰ

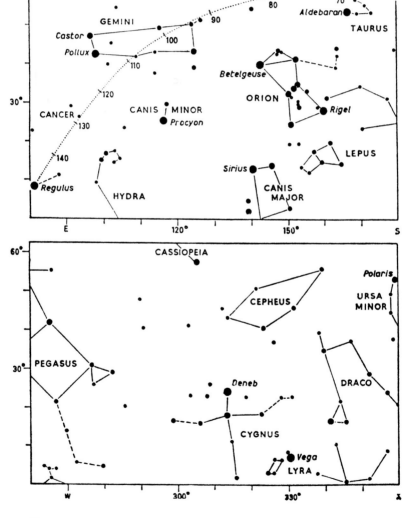

October 6 at   3ʰ   October 21 at   2ʰ
November 6 at   1ʰ   November 21 at midnight
December 6 at 23ʰ   December 21 at   22ʰ
January 6 at 21ʰ   January 21 at   20ʰ
February 6 at 19ʰ   February 21 at   18ʰ

12R

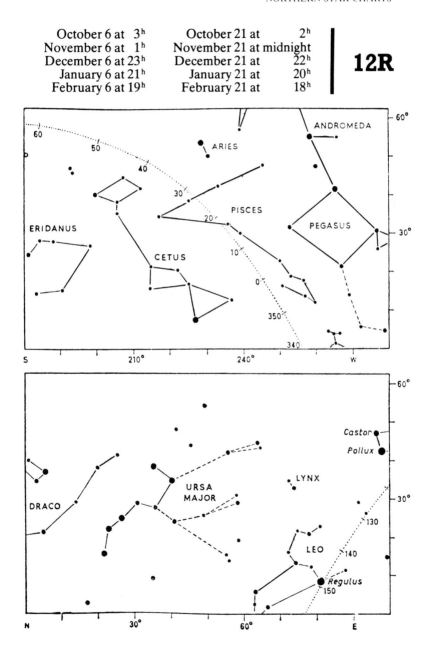

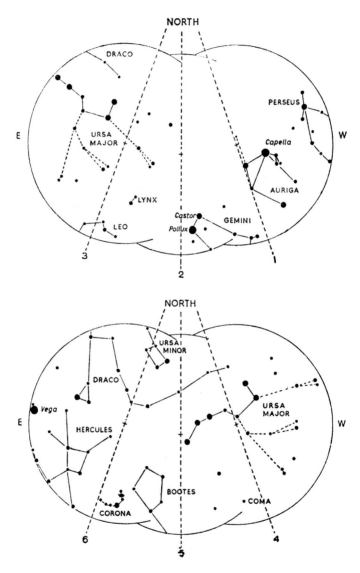

Northern Hemisphere Overhead Stars

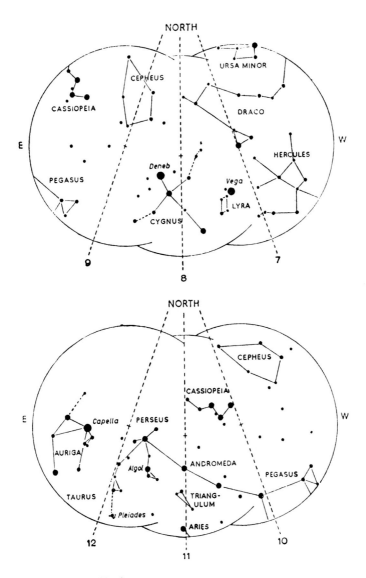

Northern Hemisphere Overhead Stars

1L

October 6 at 5^h	October 21 at 4^h
November 6 at 3^h	November 21 at 2^h
December 6 at 1^h	December 21 at midnight
January 6 at 23^h	January 21 at 22^h
February 6 at 21^h	February 21 at 20^h

60°

Fornax

Rigel

ERIDANUS

ORION

Betel-geuse

Aldebaran

30°

CETUS

80 90

70 TAURUS

60

Pleiades

50

AURIGA

40

30

ARIES

PERSEUS

Capella

10 20

PISCES

W   300°   330°   N

60°

PYXIS

False Cross

VOLANS

VELA

CARINA

CHAMAELEON

30°

HYDRA

MUSCA

CRUX

APUS

CRATER

TRIANG. AUSTR.

CENTAURUS

CIRCINUS

170

180

ARA

E   120°   150°   S

October 6 at 5ʰ   October 21 at   4ʰ
November 6 at 3ʰ   November 21 at   2ʰ
December 6 at 1ʰ   December 21 at midnight
January 6 at 23ʰ   January 21 at   22ʰ
February 6 at 21ʰ   February 21 at   20ʰ

1R

2L

November 6 at 5ʰ	November 21 at 4ʰ
December 6 at 3ʰ	December 21 at 2ʰ
January 6 at 1ʰ	January 21 at midnight
February 6 at 23ʰ	February 21 at 22ʰ
March 6 at 21ʰ	March 21 at 20ʰ

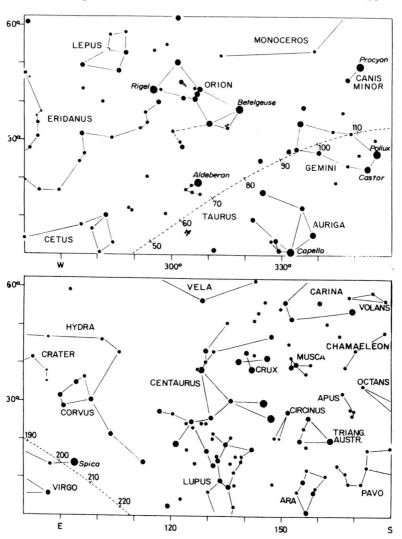

November 6 at 5^h	November 21 at 4^h	
December 6 at 3^h	December 21 at 2^h	
January 6 at 1^h	January 21 at midnight	**2R**
February 6 at 23^h	February 21 at 22^h	
March 6 at 21^h	March 21 at 20^h	

3L

January 6 at 3ʰ	January 21 at 2ʰ
February 6 at 1ʰ	February 21 at midnight
March 6 at 23ʰ	March 21 at 22ʰ
April 6 at 21ʰ	April 21 at 20ʰ
May 6 at 19ʰ	May 21 at 18ʰ

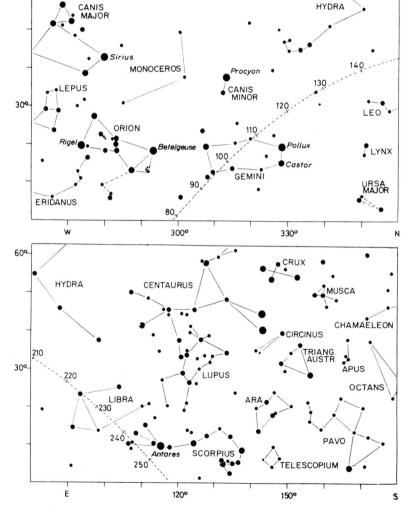

January 6 at 3ʰ   January 21 at   2ʰ
February 6 at 1ʰ   February 21 at midnight
March 6 at 23ʰ   March 21 at   22ʰ   **3R**
April 6 at 21ʰ   April 21 at   20ʰ
May 6 at 19ʰ   May 21 at   18ʰ

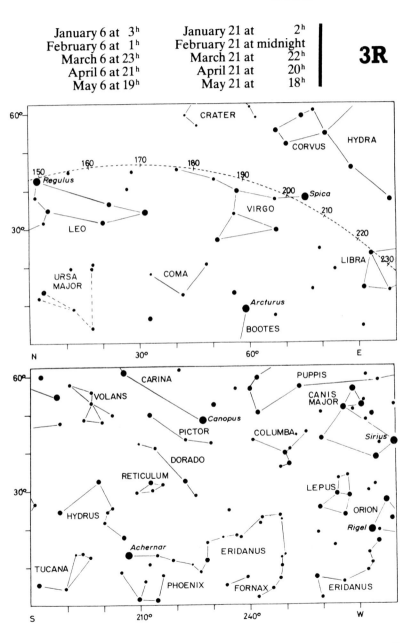

45

4L

February 6 at 3^h
March 6 at 1^h
April 6 at 23^h
May 6 at 21^h
June 6 at 19^h

February 21 at 2^h
March 21 at midnight
April 21 at 22^h
May 21 at 20^h
June 21 at 18^h

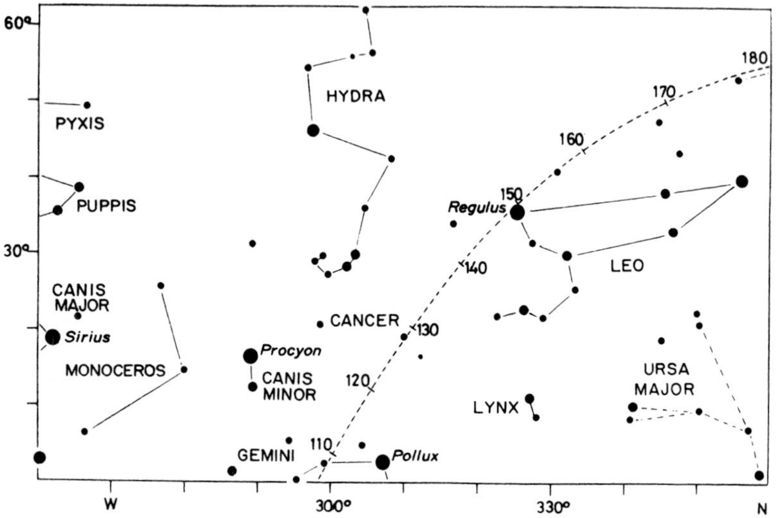

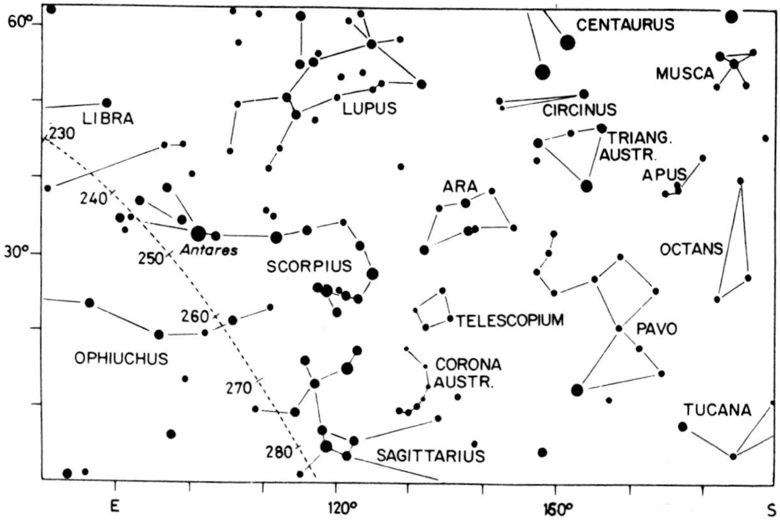

February 6 at 3ʰ	February 21 at 2ʰ	
March 6 at 1ʰ	March 21 at midnight	
April 6 at 23ʰ	April 21 at 22ʰ	**4R**
May 6 at 21ʰ	May 21 at 20ʰ	
June 6 at 19ʰ	June 21 at 18ʰ	

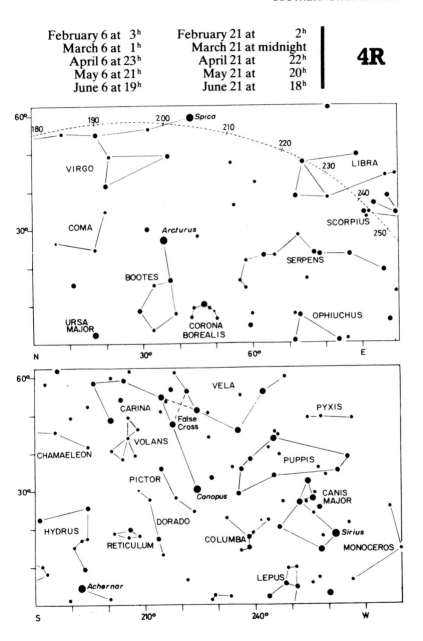

5L

March 6 at 3^h	March 21 at 2^h
April 6 at 1^h	April 21 at midnight
May 6 at 23^h	May 21 at 22^h
June 6 at 21^h	June 21 at 20^h
July 6 at 19^h	July 21 at 18^h

March 6 at 3ʰ	March 21 at 2ʰ
April 6 at 1ʰ	April 21 at midnight
May 6 at 23ʰ	May 21 at 22ʰ
June 6 at 21ʰ	June 21 at 20ʰ
July 6 at 19ʰ	July 21 at 18ʰ

5R

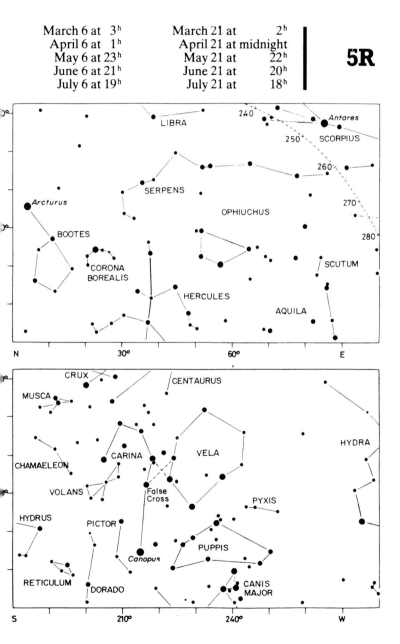

6L

March 6 at 5ʰ	March 21 at 4ʰ
April 6 at 3ʰ	April 21 at 2ʰ
May 6 at 1ʰ	May 21 at midnight
June 6 at 23ʰ	June 21 at 22ʰ
July 6 at 21ʰ	July 21 at 20ʰ

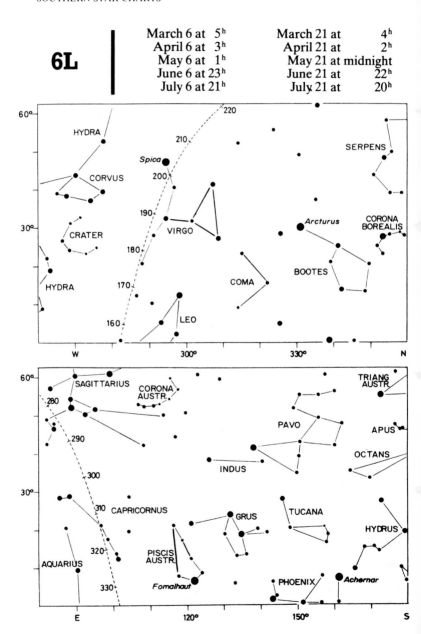

March 6 at 5ʰ	March 21 at 4ʰ	
April 6 at 3ʰ	April 21 at 2ʰ	**6R**
May 6 at 1ʰ	May 21 at midnight	
June 6 at 23ʰ	June 21 at 22ʰ	
July 6 at 21ʰ	July 21 at 20ʰ	

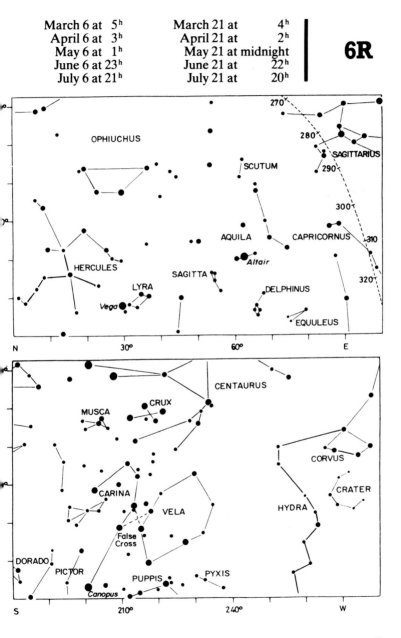

7L

April 6 at	5ʰ	April 21 at	4ʰ
May 6 at	3ʰ	May 21 at	2ʰ
June 6 at	1ʰ	June 21 at midnight	
July 6 at	23ʰ	July 21 at	22ʰ
August 6 at	21ʰ	August 21 at	20ʰ

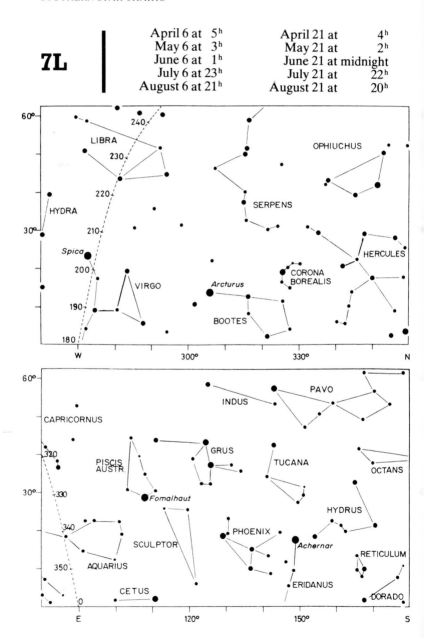

April 6 at 5ʰ   April 21 at   4ʰ
May 6 at 3ʰ   May 21 at   2ʰ
June 6 at 1ʰ   June 21 at midnight   **7R**
July 6 at 23ʰ   July 21 at   22ʰ
August 6 at 21ʰ   August 21 at   20ʰ

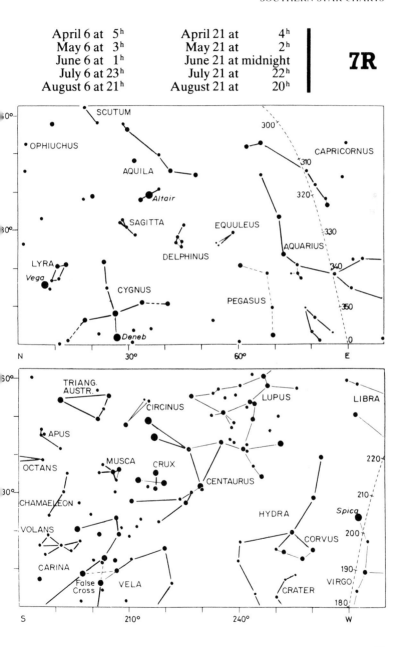

8L

May 6 at 5ʰ	May 21 at 4ʰ
June 6 at 3ʰ	June 21 at 2ʰ
July 6 at 1ʰ	July 21 at midnight
August 6 at 23ʰ	August 21 at 22ʰ
September 6 at 21ʰ	September 21 at 20ʰ

May 6 at 5^h	May 21 at 4^h
June 6 at 3^h	June 21 at 2^h
July 6 at 1^h	July 21 at midnight
August 6 at 23^h	August 21 at 22^h
September 6 at 21^h	September 21 at 20^h

8R

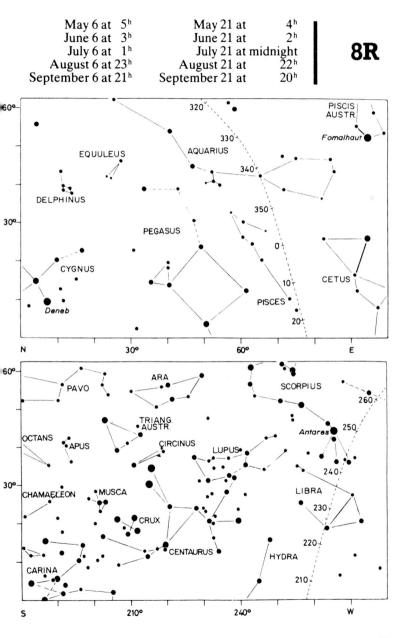

9L

June 6 at 5ʰ	June 21 at 4ʰ
July 6 at 3ʰ	July 21 at 2ʰ
August 6 at 1ʰ	August 21 at midnight
September 6 at 23ʰ	September 21 at 22ʰ
October 6 at 21ʰ	October 21 at 20ʰ

June 6 at 5ʰ	June 21 at 4ʰ
July 6 at 3ʰ	July 21 at 2ʰ
August 6 at 1ʰ	August 21 at midnight
September 6 at 23ʰ	September 21 at 22ʰ
October 6 at 21ʰ	October 21 at 20ʰ

9R

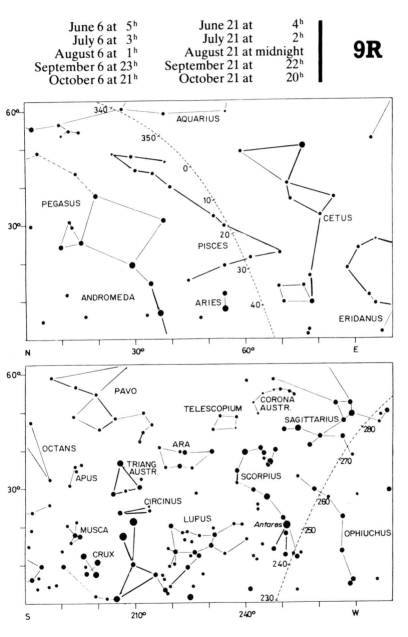

10L

July 6 at 5ʰ	July 21 at 4ʰ
August 6 at 3ʰ	August 21 at 2ʰ
September 6 at 1ʰ	September 21 at midnight
October 6 at 23ʰ	October 21 at 22ʰ
November 6 at 21ʰ	November 21 at 20ʰ

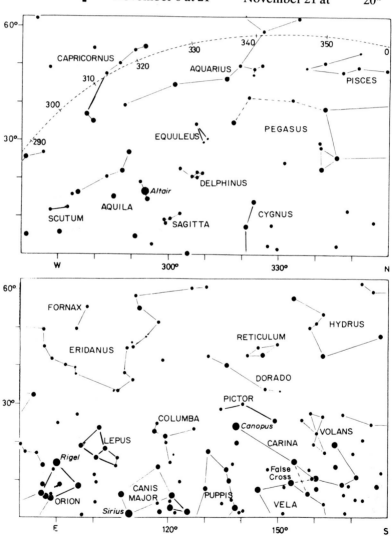

July 6 at 5ʰ	July 21 at 4ʰ	
August 6 at 3ʰ	August 21 at 2ʰ	
September 6 at 1ʰ	September 21 at midnight	**10R**
October 6 at 23ʰ	October 21 at 22ʰ	
November 6 at 21ʰ	November 21 at 20ʰ	

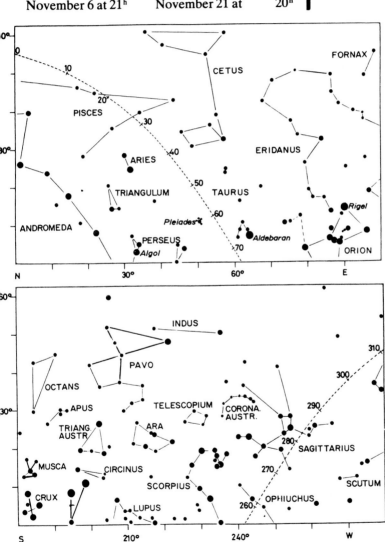

11L

August 6 at 5ʰ	August 21 at 4ʰ
September 6 at 3ʰ	September 21 at 2ʰ
October 6 at 1ʰ	October 21 at midnight
November 6 at 23ʰ	November 21 at 22ʰ
December 6 at 21ʰ	December 21 at 20ʰ

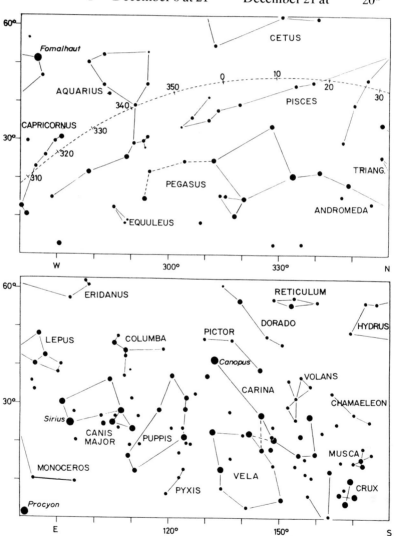

August 6 at 5ʰ   August 21 at   4ʰ
September 6 at 3ʰ   September 21 at   2ʰ
October 6 at 1ʰ   October 21 at midnight
November 6 at 23ʰ   November 21 at   22ʰ
December 6 at 21ʰ   December 21 at   20ʰ

11R

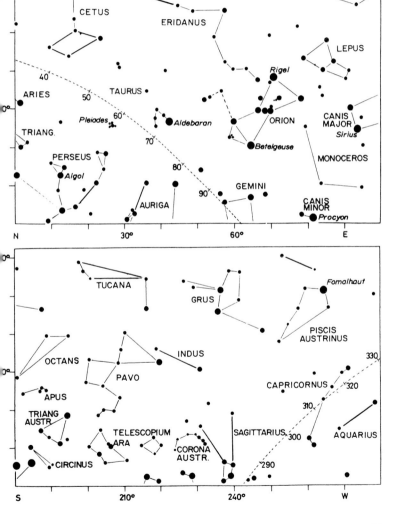

12L

September 6 at 5^h	September 21 at 4^h
October 6 at 3^h	October 21 at 2^h
November 6 at 1^h	November 21 at midnight
December 6 at 23^h	December 21 at 22^h
January 6 at 21^h	January 21 at 20^h

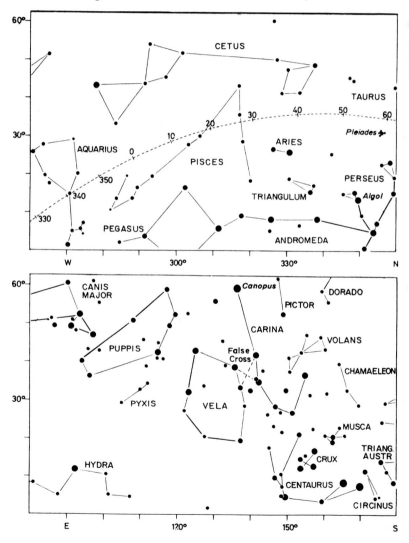

September 6 at 5^h September 21 at   4^h
October 6 at 3^h October 21 at   2^h
November 6 at 1^h November 21 at midnight
December 6 at 23^h December 21 at   22^h
January 6 at 21^h January 21 at   20^h

12R

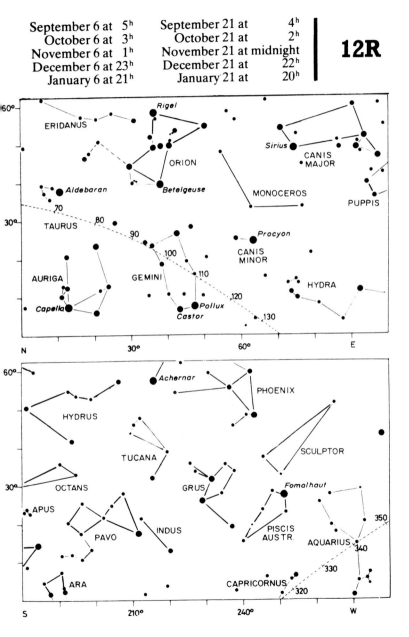

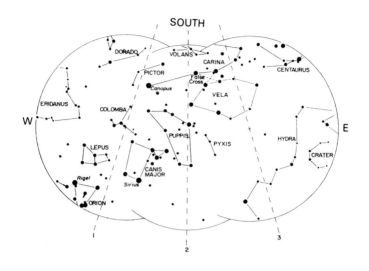

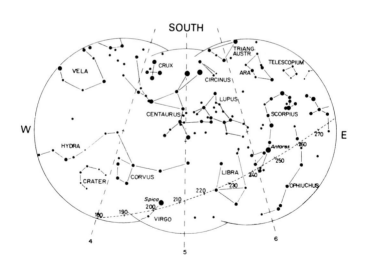

Southern Hemisphere Overhead Stars

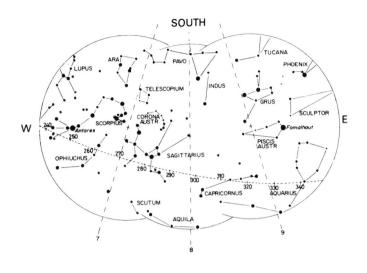

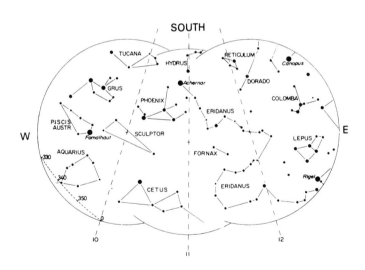

Southern Hemisphere Overhead Stars

The Planets and the Ecliptic

The paths of the planets about the Sun all lie close to the plane of the ecliptic, which is marked for us in the sky by the apparent path of the Sun among the stars, and is shown on the star charts by a broken line. The Moon and planets will always be found close to this line, never departing from it by more than about 7 degrees. Thus the planets are most favourably placed for observation when the ecliptic is well displayed, and this means that it should be as high in the sky as possible. This avoids the difficulty of finding a clear horizon, and also overcomes the problem of atmospheric absorption, which greatly reduces the light of the stars. Thus a star at an altitude of 10 degrees suffers a loss of 60 per cent of its light, which corresponds to a whole magnitude; at an altitude of only 4 degrees, the loss may amount to two magnitudes.

The position of the ecliptic in the sky is therefore of great importance, and since it is tilted at about 23½ degrees to the Equator, it is only at certain times of the day or year that it is displayed to the best advantage. It will be realized that the Sun (and therefore the ecliptic) is at its highest in the sky at noon in midsummer, and at its lowest at noon in midwinter. Allowing for the daily motion of the sky, these times lead to the fact that the ecliptic is highest at midnight in winter, at sunset in the spring, at noon in summer and at sunrise in the autumn. Hence these are the best times to see the planets. Thus, if Venus is an evening object in the western sky after sunset, it will be seen to best advantage if this occurs in the spring, when the ecliptic is high in the sky and slopes down steeply to the horizon. This means that the planet is not only higher in the sky, but will remain for a much longer period above the horizon. For similar reasons, a morning object will be seen at its best on autumn mornings before sunrise, when the ecliptic is high in the east. The outer planets, which can come to opposition (i.e. opposite the Sun), are best seen when opposition occurs in the winter months, when the ecliptic is high in the sky at midnight.

The seasons are reversed in the Southern Hemisphere, spring beginning at the September Equinox, when the Sun crosses the Equator on its way south, summer beginning at the December

Solstice, when the Sun is highest in the southern sky, and so on. Thus, the times when the ecliptic is highest in the sky, and therefore best placed for observing the planets, may be summarized as follows:

	Midnight	Sunrise	Noon	Sunset
Northern lats.	December	September	June	March
Southern lats.	June	March	December	September

In addition to the daily rotation of the celestial sphere from east to west, the planets have a motion of their own among the stars. The apparent movement is generally *direct*, i.e. to the east, in the direction of increasing longitude, but for a certain period (which depends on the distance of the planet) this apparent motion is reversed. With the outer planets this *retrograde* motion occurs about the time of opposition. Owing to the different inclination of the orbits of these planets, the actual effect is to cause the apparent path to form a loop, or sometimes an S-shaped curve. The same effect is present in the motion of the inferior planets, Mercury and Venus, but it is not so obvious, since it always occurs at the time of inferior conjunction.

The inferior planets, Mercury and Venus, move in smaller orbits than that of the Earth, and so are always seen near the Sun. They are most obvious at the times of greatest angular distance from the Sun (greatest elongation), which may reach 28 degrees for Mercury, or 47 degrees for Venus. They are seen as evening objects in the western sky after sunset (at eastern elongations) or as morning objects in the eastern sky before sunrise (at western elongations). The succession of phenomena, conjunctions and elongations, always follows the same order, but the intervals between them are not equal. Thus, if either planet is moving round the far side of its orbit its motion will be to the east, in the same direction in which the Sun appears to be moving. It therefore takes much longer for the planet to overtake the Sun – that is, to come to superior conjunction – than it does when moving round to inferior conjunction, between Sun and Earth. The intervals given in the following table are average values; they remain fairly constant in the case of Venus, which travels in an almost circular orbit. In the case of Mercury, however, conditions vary widely because of the great eccentricity and inclination of the planet's orbit.

		Mercury	Venus
Inferior conj.	to Elongation West	22 days	72 days
Elongation West	to Superior conj.	36 days	220 days
Superior conj.	to Elongation East	36 days	220 days
Elongation East	to Inferior conj.	22 days	72 days

The greatest brilliancy of Venus always occurs about 36 days before or after inferior conjunction. This will be about a month *after* greatest eastern elongation (as an evening object), or a month *before* greatest western elongation (as a morning object). No such rule can be given for Mercury, because its distance from the Earth and the Sun can vary over a wide range.

Mercury is not likely to be seen unless a clear horizon is available. It is seldom seen as much as 10 degrees above the horizon in the twilight sky in northern latitudes, but this figure is often exceeded in the Southern Hemisphere. This favourable condition arises because the maximum elongation of 28 degrees can occur only when the planet is at aphelion (farthest from the Sun), and this point lies well south of the Equator. Northern observers must be content with smaller elongations, which may be as little as 18 degrees at perihelion. In general, it may be said that the most favourable times for seeing Mercury as an evening object will be in spring, some days before greatest eastern elongation; in autumn, it may be seen as a morning object some days after greatest western elongation.

Venus is the brightest of the planets and may be seen on occasions in broad daylight. Like Mercury, it is alternately a morning and an evening object, and it will be highest in the sky when it is a morning object in autumn, or an evening object in spring. The phenomena of Venus given in the table above can occur only in the months of January, April, June, August and November, and it will be realized that they do not all lead to favourable apparitions of the planet. In fact, Venus is to be seen at its best as an evening object in northern latitudes when eastern elongation occurs in June. The planet is then well north of the Sun in the preceding spring months, and is a brilliant object in the evening sky over a long period. In the Southern Hemisphere a November elongation is best. For similar reasons, Venus gives a prolonged display as a morning object in the months following western elongation in November (in northern latitudes) or in June (in the Southern Hemisphere).

The superior planets, which travel in orbits larger than that of the Earth, differ from Mercury and Venus in that they can be seen opposite the Sun in the sky. The superior planets are morning objects after conjunction with the Sun, rising earlier each day until they come to opposition. They will then be nearest to the Earth (and therefore at their brightest), and will then be on the meridian at midnight, due south in northern latitudes, but due north in the Southern Hemisphere. After opposition they are evening objects, setting earlier each evening until they set in the west with the Sun at the next conjunction. The change in brightness about the time of opposition is most noticeable in the case of Mars, whose distance from Earth can vary considerably and rapidly. The other superior planets are at such great distances that there is very little change in brightness from one opposition to another. The effect of altitude is, however, of some importance, for at a December opposition in northern latitudes the planets will be among the stars of Taurus or Gemini, and can then be at an altitude of more than 60 degrees in southern England. At a summer opposition, when the planet is in Sagittarius, it may only rise to about 15 degrees above the southern horizon, and so makes a less impressive appearance. In the Southern Hemisphere, the reverse conditions apply, a June opposition being the best, with the planet in Sagittarius at an altitude which can reach 80 degrees above the northern horizon for observers in South Africa.

Mars, whose orbit is appreciably eccentric, comes nearest to the Earth at an opposition at the end of August. It may then be brighter even than Jupiter, but rather low in the sky in Aquarius for northern observers, though very well placed for those in southern latitudes. These favourable oppositions occur every fifteen or seventeen years (1956, 1971, 1988, 2003) but in the Northern Hemisphere the planet is probably better seen at an opposition in the autumn or winter months, when it is higher in the sky. Oppositions of Mars occur at an average interval of 780 days, and during this time the planet makes a complete circuit of the sky.

Jupiter is always a bright planet, and comes to opposition a month later each year, having moved, roughly speaking, from one Zodiacal constellation to the next.

Saturn moves much more slowly than Jupiter, and may remain in the same constellation for several years. The brightness of Saturn depends on the aspects of its rings, as well as on the distance from Earth and Sun. The rings were inclined towards the Earth and Sun in 1980 and are now past their maximum opening. The next passage of both Earth and Sun through the ring-plane will not occur until 1995.

Uranus, *Neptune*, and *Pluto* are hardly likely to attract the attention of observers without adequate instruments.

Phases of the Moon 1994

	New Moon				First Quarter				Full Moon				Last Quarter		
	d	h	m		d	h	m		d	h	m		d	h	m
												Jan.	5	00	01
Jan.	11	23	10	Jan.	19	20	27	Jan.	27	13	23	Feb.	3	08	06
Feb.	10	14	30	Feb.	18	17	47	Feb.	26	01	15	Mar.	4	16	53
Mar.	12	07	05	Mar.	20	12	14	Mar.	27	11	10	Apr.	3	02	55
Apr.	11	00	17	Apr.	19	02	34	Apr.	25	19	45	May	2	14	32
May	10	17	07	May	18	12	50	May	25	03	39	June	1	04	02
June	9	08	26	June	16	19	57	June	23	11	33	June	30	19	31
July	8	21	37	July	16	01	12	July	22	20	16	July	30	12	40
Aug.	7	08	45	Aug.	14	05	57	Aug.	21	06	47	Aug.	29	06	41
Sept.	5	18	33	Sept.	12	11	34	Sept.	19	20	01	Sept.	28	00	23
Oct.	5	03	55	Oct.	11	19	17	Oct.	19	12	18	Oct.	27	16	44
Nov.	3	13	36	Nov.	10	06	14	Nov.	18	06	57	Nov.	26	07	04
Dec.	2	23	54	Dec.	9	21	06	Dec.	18	02	17	Dec.	25	19	06

All times are G.M.T.

Longitudes of the Sun, Moon and Planets in 1994

DATE		Sun	Moon	Venus	Mars	Jupiter	Saturn
		°	°	°	°	°	°
January	6	285	209	283	283	221	327
	21	301	43	301	294	222	329
February	6	317	261	322	307	224	331
	21	332	88	340	318	225	333
March	6	345	271	357	329	225	334
	21	0	96	15	340	224	336
April	6	16	320	35	353	223	338
	21	31	144	53	4	221	339
May	6	45	354	72	16	219	341
	21	60	182	89	27	217	341
June	6	75	38	109	40	216	342
	21	89	235	126	50	215	342
July	6	104	70	144	61	215	342
	21	118	274	160	72	215	342
August	6	133	116	178	83	217	341
	21	148	324	193	92	218	340
September	6	163	166	209	103	221	339
	21	178	11	220	112	223	338
October	6	193	204	227	121	226	337
	21	207	44	227	129	229	336
November	6	223	258	218	137	233	336
	21	238	88	213	143	236	336
December	6	254	295	215	148	239	336
	21	269	121	224	152	242	337

Longitude of *Uranus* 294°
Neptune 292°

Moon: Longitude of ascending node
Jan. 1: 241°   Dec. 31: 222°

Mercury moves so quickly among the stars that it is not possible to indicate its position on the star charts at a convenient interval. The monthly notes must be consulted for the best times at which the planet may be seen.

The positions of the other planets are given in the table on the previous page. This gives the apparent longitudes on dates which correspond to those of the star charts, and the position of the planet may at once be found near the ecliptic at the given longitude.

Examples
In the Southern Hemisphere two planets are seen in the eastern morning sky in late April. Identify them.

The southern star chart 7R shows the eastern sky at April 21^d04^h and shows longitudes 300°–0°. Reference to the table on page 71 gives the longitude of Mars as 4° and that of Saturn as 339°, on April 21. Thus these planets are found in the eastern sky and the one lower down is Mars.

The positions of the Sun and Moon can be plotted on the star maps in the same manner as for the planets. The average daily motion of the Sun is 1°, and of the Moon 13°. For the Moon an indication of its position relative to the ecliptic may be obtained from a consideration of its longitude relative to that of the ascending node. The latter changes only slowly during the year as will be seen from the values given on the previous page. Let us call the difference in longitude of Moon-node, d. Then if d = 0°, 180° or 360° the Moon is on the ecliptic. If d = 90° the Moon is 5° north of the ecliptic and if d = 270° the Moon is 5° south of the ecliptic.

On April 21 the Moon's longitude is given as 144° and the longitude of the node is found by interpolation to be about 235°. Thus d = 269° and the Moon is about 5° south of the ecliptic. Its position may be plotted on northern star charts 3R, 4R, 5R and southern star charts 3L, 4L, 5L.

Events in 1994

There will be three eclipses, two of the Sun and one of the Moon.

May 10: annular eclipse of the Sun – Americas, Europe.
May 25: partial eclipse of the Moon – Africa, Europe, Americas.
November 3: total eclipse of the Sun – South America, Southern Africa.

THE PLANETS

Mercury may be seen more easily from northern latitudes in the evenings about the time of greatest eastern elongation (February 4) and in the mornings around greatest western elongation (November 6). In the Southern Hemisphere the dates are March 19 (morning) and September 26 (evening).

Venus is visible in the evenings from late February to October and in the mornings from November onwards.

Mars is visible in the mornings from March onwards.

Jupiter is at opposition on April 30.

Saturn is at opposition on September 1.

Uranus is at opposition on July 17.

Neptune is at opposition on July 14.

Pluto is at opposition on May 17.

JANUARY

New Moon: January 11   *Full Moon:* January 27

EARTH is at perihelion (nearest to the Sun) on January 2 at a distance of 147 million kilometres (91,440,000 miles).

MERCURY is at superior conjunction on January 3 and therefore too close to the Sun for observation. However, by the end of the month observers in the Northern Hemisphere should be able to detect the planet low above the south-western horizon around the time of end of evening civil twilight. Observers in the British Isles should start looking for Mercury (magnitude −0.9) from January 27 onwards but observers in the Southern Hemisphere should wait until March.

VENUS passes slowly through superior conjunction on January 17 and therefore remains too close to the Sun for observation throughout the month.

MARS, having passed through conjunction only five days before the beginning of January, is too close to the Sun for observation.

JUPITER, magnitude −1.9, is a bright morning object in the south-eastern sky before twilight inhibits observation. The path of Jupiter amongst the stars is shown in Figure 2, given with the notes for April.

SATURN, magnitude +0.9, is an evening object in the south-western sky. By the end of the month it is becoming a difficult object to detect, being very low before the twilight has faded sufficiently for it to be visible. Saturn is in Aquarius.

EQUATORIAL STARS. Throughout January, Orion is dominant in the evening sky. This is true for both the Northern and Southern

Hemispheres of the globe, because Orion is cut by the celestial equator; thus of its two leaders, Betelgeux is well north of the equator and Rigel well south. Orion is therefore visible from every inhabited country – though if, as expected, an observatory is established right at the South Pole, observers there will find that Rigel is above the horizon all the time and Betelgeux never!

It is interesting to check and see which bright stars are very close to the equator. There are, in fact, fewer of them than might be expected. There are only ten stars above the fourth magnitude which are within two degrees of the equator; they are as follows (positions given for epoch 2000):

Star	Declination			Magnitude
	°	′	″	
Gamma Aquarii	−01	23	14	3.8
Zeta Aquarii	−00	01	13	3.6
Theta Aquilæ	−00	49	17	3.2
Iota Hydræ	−01	08	34	3.9
Lambda Ophiuchi	+01	59	02	3.8
Delta Orionis	−00	17	57	2.2
Epsilon Orionis	−01	12	07	1.7
Zeta Orionis	−01	56	34	1.8
Eta Virginis	−00	40	00	3.9
Gamma Virginis	−01	26	57	2.7

Taking the magnitude limit down to 4.75, we can add fifteen more stars: Pi Aquarii (4.7), Eta Aquarii (4.0), Nu Aquilæ (4.7), Iota Aquilæ (4.4), Delta Ceti (4.1), Tau^2 Hydræ (4.6), Upsilon Leonis (4.3), Delta Monocerotis (4.1), 28 Monocerotis (4.7), 41 Ophiuchi (4.7), 68 Ophiuchi (4.4), Pi^6 Orionis (4.5), Omicron Orionis (4.7), 31 Orionis (4.7) and Alpha Sextantis (4.5).

Equatorial stars may be used to find the diameter of a telescopic field. Observe the time taken for the star to pass centrally across the field from one side to the other. Express this time in minutes and seconds; multiply by 15, and you will have the diameter of the field in minutes and seconds of arc.

MINTAKA. One of our 'equatorial stars', Mintaka or Delta Orionis – the northernmost star of the Hunter's Belt – is of decided interest. It is a highly luminous giant, with an absolute magnitude of −6.1, giving a luminosity 22,000 times that of the Sun; the spectral type is

09.5, and the distance is 2350 light-years. In 1834 Sir John Herschel announced that it was variable, and it is included in Chambers' catalogue of variable stars contained in his *Handbook of Astronomy*, one of the classic works of the last century. The range was given as magnitude 2¼ to 2¾, and the star was classed as irregular, but Chambers adds a note: 'Schönfeld finds no regular period, but Auwers suggests 16 days, with minima nearly in the middle interval between maxima'.

This is strange, because Mintaka does not show variations marked enough to be visible with the naked eye – at least, not nowadays! It is in fact an eclipsing binary, with a range of from magnitude 2.20 to 2.35 and a period of 5.73 days.

There is a companion visible with small telescopes; magnitude 6.3, separation 52".6, position angle 359°. Whether the companion is genuinely associated with Mintaka is uncertain; if it is, the distance between the two must be over half a light-year.

In 1904 Hartmann, at the Potsdam Observatory, was studying the spectrum of Mintaka when he found that some lines, due to calcium, did not take part in the general Doppler shifting. He correctly suggested that these lines were due to interstellar material, and not to the star itself.

FEBRUARY

New Moon: February 10   *Full Moon:* February 26

MERCURY is at greatest eastern elongation (18°) on February 4. For the first half of the month observers in northern and equatorial latitudes should be able to see Mercury as an evening object low above the south-western horizon, around the time of end of evening civil twilight, its magnitude ranging from −0.8 to +2.0 during this period. The planet is unsuitably placed for observation by those in the Southern Hemisphere until nearly ten days after it passes through inferior conjunction (which occurs on February 20). Then it is a morning object in the east before sunrise (see Figure 1 given with the notes for March).

VENUS remains too close to the Sun for observation for most of the month. However, during the last ten days it is visible in the evenings for a very short while after sunset, low in the west-south-western sky, for observers in the British Isles. Its magnitude is −3.9. For observers in the Southern Hemisphere Venus is still too close to the Sun for observation.

MARS is still too close to the Sun for observation.

JUPITER is a bright morning object with a magnitude of −2.1. By the end of the month it is visible above the east-south-eastern horizon shortly after midnight.

SATURN, magnitude +0.9, is lost to view by observers in northern temperate latitudes. Observers further south may possibly detect it low on the south-western horizon as the evening twilight fades, but only for the first few days of the month. Saturn passes through conjunction on February 21, and is thus unobservable for the remainder of the month.

ENCKE'S COMET. Encke's Comet reaches perihelion on February 9. It will certainly not be spectacular, but it is an object of special interest.

It was first recorded on January 17, 1786, by Pierre Méchain – who was a contemporary of Messier, and virtually his equal as a comet-hunter. The magnitude was then 5, so that the comet was a naked-eye object, and there was a short tail. Observations were not numerous enough for a reliable orbit to be computed. It was next discovered on November 7, 1795 by Caroline Herschel; it was again lost, to be seen again on October 20, 1805 when it was discovered almost simultaneously by Pons and Bouvard. This time the magnitude was 4, and there was a 3° tail. Pons found it again on November 26, 1818. J. F. Encke concluded that the 1818 comet was identical with those of 1805, 1795, and 1786, and that the period was 3.3 years. He predicted a return for 1822, and on June 2 of that year C. L. Rumker, in Australia, recovered it, almost exactly where Encke had expected; the magnitude was 4.5.

Since then it has been seen at every return except that of 1944, when it was badly placed in the sky and most astronomers were handicapped by wartime conditions. In 1852 a 90 arc-minute tail developed, but during the twentieth century the comet has never reached naked-eye visibility, and clearly this fading is genuine. It has even been suggested that the comet will 'die' before the year 2000. However, this does not seem likely – and astronomers would be sad to say farewell to an old friend! Nowadays the comet can be followed throughout its orbit. The aphelion distance is about 380,000,000 miles, so that the comet never recedes as far as the orbit of Jupiter.

The period is shorter than for any other periodical comet. For a time it was thought that the record might be broken; a comet discovered in 1949 by A. G. Wilson and R. S. Harrington had a computed period of only 2.3 years. The comet was not seen again for decades – and when recovered, it was taken for an asteroid and given an asteroidal number: 4015. Only later was it realized that Asteroid 4015 and Comet Wilson–Harrington were identical. There is no trace of a tail now, though one was photographed in 1949, and the episode adds force to the suggestion that some small asteroids may be dead comets which have lost all their volatiles.

Incidentally, it has also been suggested that the object which hit Siberia in 1908, and devastated a wide area of tundra, was a fragment of Encke's Comet. However, the evidence is very slender, and we do not really know the nature of the Siberian impactor.

SIRIUS. Sirius, the 'Dog-star', is at its best during evenings in February. It is much brighter than any other star; as seen from

Britain it seems to flash various colours, because it is always rather low down – even though it is in fact pure white. From southern countries such as Australia the twinkling is much less, because Sirius is higher up.

Sirius owes its eminence to the fact that it is close by stellar standards; the distance is a mere 8.6 light-years, and the luminosity is 26 times that of the Sun. It is a glow-worm when compared with Canopus, which (according to the authoritative Cambridge catalogue) is 200,000 times as luminous as the Sun. It is interesting to compare the two; Sirius is the brighter by three-quarters of a magnitude. (Of course, Canopus is too far south to be seen from Britain.)

MARCH

New Moon: March 12   *Full Moon:* March 27

Summer Time in Great Britain and Northern Ireland commences on March 27.

Equinox: March 20

MERCURY is a morning object for observers in equatorial and southern latitudes. For observers in southern latitudes this will be the most favourable morning apparition of the year. Figure 1 shows, for observers in latitude S.35°, the changes in azimuth (true bearing from the north through east, south, and west) and altitude of Mercury on successive mornings when the Sun is 6° below the horizon. This condition is known as the beginning of morning civil twilight, and in this latitude and at this time of year occurs about 30 minutes before sunrise. The changes in the brightness of the planet are indicated by the relative sizes of the circles marking Mercury's position at five-day intervals. It will be noticed that Mercury is at its brightest after it reaches greatest western elongation (28°) on March 19. During the month its magnitude brightens from +1.8 to 0.0. Mercury is not visible to observers in the British Isles.

VENUS, magnitude −3.9, is visible in the evenings, low above the western horizon for a short while after sunset. However, Venus is moving northwards in declination and observers in the Southern Hemisphere will have difficulty in detecting the planet.

MARS, towards the end of the month, is very gradually emerging from the morning twilight, becoming visible low in the eastern sky before the sky gets too bright for observation. The magnitude of Mars is +1.2. However, observers in northern temperate latitudes will have to wait until June before seeing the planet.

JUPITER, magnitude −2.3, is moving towards opposition and therefore is visible for the greater part of the night.

SATURN is too close to the Sun for observation at first but gradually becomes visible as a morning object during the second part of the month, though only to observers in equatorial and southern latitudes.

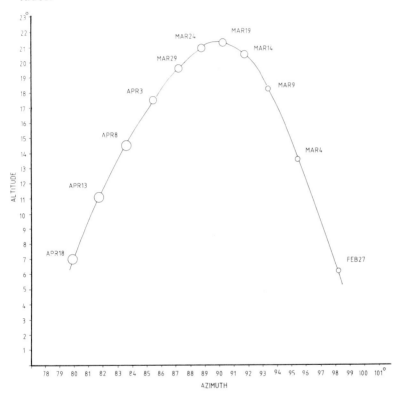

Figure 1. Morning apparition of Mercury for latitude S.35°.

MARINER 10 AT MERCURY. Only one space-craft has so far been sent to Mercury; this was Mariner 10, which made its first close approach to the planet twenty years ago – on March 29, 1974.

Before Mariner, our knowledge of Mercury was very incomplete. The planet is awkward to observe from Earth, because it is always inconveniently close to the Sun in the sky, and never comes much within fifty million miles of us. Telescopes will show little. The best pre-Space Age map was that compiled by E. M. Antoniadi, using the Meudon 33-inch refractor, but even this has been found to be very inaccurate. Moreover, Antoniadi believed that Mercury had an atmosphere substantial enough to support dust-clouds, and he went so far as to claim that the surface obscurations were 'more frequent and obliterating than those of Mars'.

Mariner 10 showed that this is not true. The atmosphere is negligible, with a ground density of around 10^{-10} millibar; there is however an appreciable magnetic field, and it seems that the heavy iron core, probably larger than the whole globe of the Moon, contains 80 per cent of the planet's mass. It is thought to be partially molten.

Mariner provided good maps of the accessible regions of the surface (less than half of the total, however). The most imposing formation is the Calöris Basin, over 800 miles in diameter, bounded by a ring of high, smooth mountain blocks. There are craters, peaks, valleys and ridges, together with broad 'intercrater plains' unlike anything found on the Moon.

It had already been established that Mercury has a rotation period of 58.6 days, two-thirds of the Mercurian 'year' of 88 days. Antoniadi had believed that the rotation period was synchronous – that is to say, identical with the orbital period – in which case there would have been a region of permanent sunlight, a region of permanent night, and a narrow zone in between over which the Sun would bob up and down over the horizon. Science fiction writers made great use of this 'twilight zone', where the temperatures would presumably be tolerable – but it does not exist. The temperature range is in fact from $+427°C$ to $-183°C$, greater than for any other planet in the Solar System.

MARCH CENTENARIES. One of the great last-century astronomers, Thomas Maclear, was born at Newtown-Stewart, in Ireland, on March 17, 1794. He intended to study medicine, but turned to astronomy, and in 1833 was appointed H.M. Astronomer at the Cape, in South Africa. He built up the observatory, and was as successful as an administrator as he was as an observer. He was knighted in 1860, and retired in 1870. He died on July 14, 1879.

Svein Rosseland, a leading Norwegian astronomer, was born on March 31, 1894. He was educated in Oslo and Copenhagen, and spent two years (1925–7) at Mount Wilson Observatory in California before returning to Norway to become Director of the Oslo

Observatory. He was concerned mainly with sunspot research and stellar spectroscopy.

Our third 'centenary' is that of Jacques Babinet, the French astronomer; he was born in Vienna on October 21, 1794, and died on October 21, 1872. He is remembered mainly as being the inventor of the polariscope.

APRIL

New Moon: April 11   *Full Moon:* April 25

MERCURY is not suitably placed for observation by observers in northern temperate latitudes. Further south it continues to be visible as a morning object for the first three weeks of the month, as will be seen from the diagram given with the notes for March. Mercury passes through superior conjunction on the last day of the month.

VENUS continues to be visible for a while in the evenings after sunset, low in the western sky. It has a magnitude of −3.9.

MARS remains unsuitably placed for observation for those in northern temperate latitudes. Observers further south will see it as a difficult morning object in the eastern sky, magnitude +1.2. There is little time for observation before the morning twilight inhibits observation.

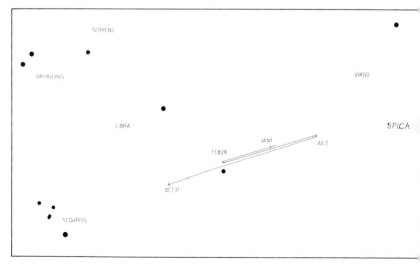

Figure 2. The path of Jupiter.

JUPITER, magnitude −2.5, is now visible throughout the hours of darkness, as it reaches opposition on April 30, in Libra. Figure 2 shows its path amongst the stars during 1994.

SATURN is a morning object, magnitude +1.0, though observers in northern temperate latitudes are unlikely to see it before the middle of the month, low above the south-eastern horizon before morning twilight inhibits observation. The path of Saturn amongst the stars is shown in Figure 6, given with the notes for August.

THE LARGEST ASTEROIDS. Asteroid No. 3, Juno, comes to opposition this month. It was discovered on September 1, 1804 by Karl Harding, who was Schröter's assistant, so that only Ceres and Pallas pre-date it. Its opposition magnitude is 8, so that it is inferior only to Vesta (6.4), Ceres (7.3), Pallas (7.5), and Iris (7.8). Yet Juno is not the third largest asteroid. The list of 'senior members', with their diameters in miles, is as follows:

Ceres	584
Vesta	358
Pallas	360 ×329 ×292
Hygeia	267
Davida	239
Interamnia	210
Cybele	191
Europa	181
Sylvia	175
Patientia	174
Euphrosyne	168
Eunomia	162
Bamberga	157
Psyche	154
Juno	179 ×143

Juno is bright, by asteroidal standards, because it is fairly reflective. Asteroids are classified into various types. These are: S (silicaceous), M (metallic), E (enstatite), D (low albedo, reddish), A (olivine), P (low albedo not unlike type M), Q (close-approach asteroids, not unlike chondrites), V (igneous rock surfaces), and U (all others). Juno is of type S, while Ceres is of type C.

Juno moves round the Sun in a period of 4.4 years; the perihelion distance is 184,000,000 miles and the aphelion distance 248,000,000 miles. It is thus a typical main-belt object, keeping strictly to that part of the Solar System between the orbits of Mars and Jupiter.

A SCIENTIFIC TRAGEDY. April 20, 1794 marked the death of one of the most charismatic astronomers of his day – Jean-Baptiste-Gaspard de Saron, usually known as Bochart de Saron.

He was born in Paris in 1730. He came of an aristocratic background, and soon showed that he had exceptional talent. He was an excellent mathematician and optical worker, and excelled also in chemistry, printing, and etching. He played a part in public life, and became a magistrate and a noted authority on legal matters; he was in fact the last Premier Président of the Parlement de Paris.

His mathematical interests brought him into touch with Charles Messier, the comet-hunter. By 1781 he was an expert computer – he was one of the first to realize that the object discovered by William Herschel was not a comet, but a new planet – and when Messier discovered a comet he would send the positions to de Saron, who would work out an orbit. This collaboration continued for years. De Saron was also known for his generosity and kindliness; he was popular everywhere – except with the leaders of the Revolution.

Tragedy lay ahead. De Saron was arrested, given a farcical trial and condemned to death. His last calculations of a cometary orbit were made while he was in prison awaiting execution; Messier received them and was able to let de Saron know that the comet had been recovered. A day or two later, de Saron went to the guillotine.

Messier himself was no mathematician, and was not a particularly accurate observer; his genius lay in the detection of comets. It is ironical that today we remember him not for his cometary work, but for his catalogue of star-clusters and nebulæ – and it is even more ironical that few people, even astronomers, remember de Saron, who contributed so much.

MAY

MERCURY is at greatest eastern elongation (23°) on May 30 and is therefore an evening object. For observers in northern temperate latitudes this will be the most favourable evening apparition of the year. Figure 3 shows, for observers in latitude N.52°, the changes in azimuth (true bearing from the north through east, south, and west) and altitude of Mercury on successive evenings when the Sun is 6° below the horizon. This condition is known as the end of evening civil twilight, and in this latitude and at this time of year occurs about 35 minutes after sunset. The changes in the brightness of the planet are indicated by the relative sizes of the circles marking Mercury's position at five-day intervals. It will be noticed that Mercury is at its brightest before it reaches greatest eastern elongation (23°) on May 30. Conditions are less favourable for observers in southern latitudes though it should be possible for them to see the planet low in the north-western sky towards the end of the month.

VENUS, magnitude −3.9, continues to be visible as an evening object, low in the western sky after sunset. Venus attains its maximum northerly declination towards the end of the month and for observers in southern Britain it sets about two hours after the Sun.

MARS is still too poorly placed for it to be visible to observers in the British Isles, where the beginning of morning twilight is getting noticeably earlier from week to week. Further south the planet is visible as a morning object in the eastern sky, magnitude +1.2.

JUPITER, which reached opposition on the last day of last month is visible throughout the hours of darkness. Its magnitude is −2.4. At closest approach, on May 1, it is 662 million kilometres (411 million miles) from the Earth.

SATURN, magnitude +1.0, continues to be visible as a morning object, visible in the south-eastern sky for several hours before dawn (though for a much shorter period of time for observers in the British Isles).

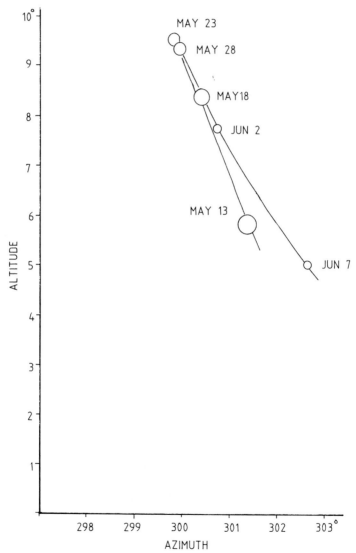

Figure 3. Evening apparition of Mercury for latitude N.52°.

LEO. Leo, the Lion, is one of the most conspicuous of the Zodiacal constellations. It is well on view during evenings in April, and is visible from every inhabited country. Regulus, the leading star, has a declination of +12 degrees.

Leo is marked by a curved line of stars, rather recalling the mirror image of a question-mark; this is called the Sickle. The rest of the constellation is made up of a triangle of stars (Denebola, Zosma, and Chort – see Figure 4). The brightest stars are:

Star		Magnitude	Spectrum	Luminosity (Sun = 1)	Distance light-years
α	Regulus	1.35	B7	130	85
γ	Algieba	1.99	K0+G7	60	91
β	Denebola	2.14	A3	17	39
δ	Zosma	2.56	A4	14	52
ε	Asad Australis	2.98	G0	525	310
θ	Chort	3.34	A2	25	78
ζ	Adhafera	3.44	F0	45	117
η		3.52	A0	10,000	1825
o	Subra	3.52	A5	12	55
ϱ		3.85	B1	15,000	2510
μ	Rassalas	3.88	K2	90	179
ι		3.94	F2	14	78
λ	Alterf	4.31	K5	100	257

There is a great range here, and it is not easy to appreciate that, for instance, the obscure-looking Rho Leonis is so much more powerful than Regulus!

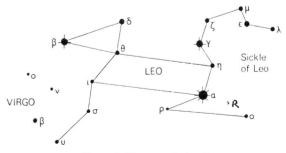

Figure 4. The constellation Leo.

A minor mystery surrounds Denebola. Some ancient astronomers ranked it as being of the first magnitude, and equal to
Regulus, but this is certainly not the case now. It does not seem to
be the sort of star to show variations, either short-term or secular,
and it is more likely that there has been an error in interpretation;
all the same, it is curious.

Algieba is a splendid double. The components are of magnitudes
2.2 and 3.5, and since the separation is 4.3 seconds of arc a small
telescope will divide them. The primary is orange, and the companion yellowish. The pair makes up a binary system, and the period is
619 years. There are two faint optical companions (magnitudes 9.2
and 9.6 respectively) at separations of 260 and 333 seconds of arc.

R Leonis is a typical Mira star, with a range of from magnitude 4.4
to 11.3 and a period of 312 days. The distance is 600 light-years, and
the peak luminosity over 200 times that of the Sun; the strong red
colour is obvious – even with binoculars when the star is near
maximum. There are also several Messier objects in Leo – the
galaxies M95 and M96, between Regulus and Iota, and M65 and
M66, between Iota and Upsilon. (Upsilon, incidentally, is an
'equatorial' star, only 49 seconds of arc south of the celestial
equator.) All four galaxies are spirals, and are easy objects in small
telescopes.

In mythology Leo was the Nemæan lion, one of the victims of
Hercules – but in the sky, the Lion is far more conspicuous than its
hunter!

THE ETA AQUARIDS. Most people remember Halley's Comet,
which attracted wide attention at its 1986 return even though it was
badly placed in the sky and never became brilliant, as it had done in
1910 and in 1835. (The next return, that of 2061, will be even
worse.) We have bade adieu to the comet for the moment, but not
to its debris; the Eta Aquarid meteors are associated with it. This is
a prolonged but not usually a brilliant shower, extending from April
24 to May 20 with a broad, multiple maximum. On occasions the
ZHR (Zenithal Hourly Rate) may exceed 30.

JUNE

New Moon: June 9   *Full Moon:* June 23

Solstice: June 21

MERCURY continues to be visible as an evening object. Those in the latitudes of the British Isles should be able to detect it low in the north-western sky at the end of civil twilight for the first week of the month (magnitude +1) and should refer to Figure 3 given with the notes for May, for further guidance. Mercury passes through inferior conjunction on June 25.

VENUS is a brilliant object in the western sky in the evenings, magnitude −4.0. Observers in northern temperate latitudes will find that, relative to the time of sunset, Venus is setting earlier even though its angular distance from the Sun continues to increase; this is because Venus is now moving southwards in declination.

MARS is a morning object, magnitude +1.2. Mars moves from Aries to Taurus and by the end of June is passing about 5° south of the Pleiades, as will be seen from an inspection of Figure 5.

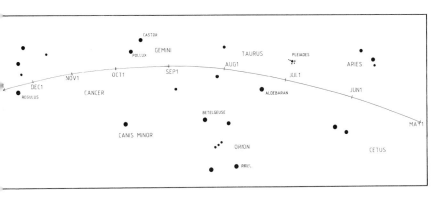

Figure 5. The path of Mars.

JUPITER, magnitude −2.3, is an evening object in Virgo. For observers in northern temperate latitudes the planet will be lost to view before midnight, by the end of the month.

SATURN is a morning object, magnitude +0.9. By the end of the month observers in the British Isles should be able to detect it low above the east-south-east horizon shortly before midnight.

TUTTLE'S COMET. A well-known periodical comet comes to perihelion this month. It was originally found by Pierre Méchain in 1790, and was then seen by Horace Tuttle in 1858. Shortly after Tuttle's discovery the comet was picked up independently by C. Bruhns from Berlin, and it became clear that the orbit was elliptical with a period of around 13 to 14 years. Tuttle suggested that it was identical with Méchain's comet of 1790, while Bruhns believed that it was the same as Comet 1785 I, discovered by Messier. Tuttle proved to be right, and the comet was accordingly named after him. It has since been seen at every return except that of 1953, when it was very badly placed. The period is 13.7 years.

On occasion, the comet has reached naked-eye visibility, though it has seldom developed an appreciable tail. The maximum magnitude during the returns since 1790 has been:

1790	5.5	1912	8.0
1858	6.5	1926	12.5
1871	7.5	1939	13.6
1885	9.5	1967	9.0
1899	10.0	1980	6.5

Unfortunately this will not be a good apparition, and the magnitude is unlikely to be much brighter than 12. However, comet observers will be paying close attention to it. It is the parent comet of the Ursid meteors, which reach their maximum on 23 December each year and which can be spectacular, as they were in 1945 and 1986.

HERMANN OBERTH. This month sees the centenary of the birth of one of the great pioneers of rocket science. Hermann Oberth was born on June 25, 1894 at Hermannstadt in Transylvania. He was Romanian, but studied in Germany, and during World War I served in the German Army; he was wounded, though not seriously. He then resumed his studies, and in 1923 published his classic book *The Rocket into Interplanetary Space*. This was the first truly scientific book to be devoted to space-flight, and the effects of its influence can hardly be over-estimated; rather, to Oberth's surprise, it even became something of a best-seller!

This was Oberth's major contribution, but he continued with his work, and in 1941 went to Peenemünde, where the rocket team headed by Wernher von Braun was busily developing the V.2 weapon. When the Royal Air Force bombed Peenemünde, in 1943, Oberth again distinguished himself by his bravery in helping to rescue those who were wounded. After the war he virtually retired from active research, though he did spend some time in the United States and was present in Mission Control when Neil Armstrong stepped out on to the surface of the Moon.

It is probably true to say that Oberth will always be remembered as one of the men who made space-flight possible, and his classic book will never be forgotten. He died in 1990.

R CORONÆ. The small but prominent constellation of Corona Borealis is well placed during June evenings. In the 'bowl' of the Crown is the irregular variable R Coronæ, which is usually on the fringe of naked-eye visibility but which may drop to very faint minimum. Another star of magnitude 6.6 is also in the 'bowl'. If you use binoculars, and see only one star instead of two, you may be sure that R Coronæ is hiding itself behind clouds of soot in its atmosphere!

JULY

EARTH is at aphelion (farthest from the Sun) on July 5 at a distance of 152 million kilometres (94.5 million miles).

MERCURY attains its greatest elongation west of the Sun (21°) on July 17 and is therefore a morning object. For observers in the British Isles it is a very difficult object to detect; the only hope of detecting it would be within a few days of July 21, low in the east-north-eastern sky at the time of beginning of morning civil twilight. Conditions are better for observers further south as Mercury will be slightly higher in the sky, and considerably brighter towards the end of the month. On July 19 Mercury's magnitude is +0.2 while on July 31 it is −1.1.

VENUS, magnitude −4.1, continues to be visible as an evening object, above the western horizon after sunset. Venus passes 1°N. of Regulus on July 10, though this will occur before dusk, for observers in the British Isles.

MARS, magnitude +1.2, is a morning object in Taurus, passing between the Pleiades and the Hyades early in the month.

JUPITER continues to be visible as an evening object, magnitude −2.1.

SATURN, magnitude +0.8, is a morning object in Aquarius.

URANUS is at opposition on July 17, in Sagittarius. The planet is only just visible to the naked-eye under the best of conditions, since its magnitude is +5.6. In a small telescope it appears as a slightly greenish disk. At opposition Uranus is 2790 million kilometres (1734 million miles) from the Earth.

NEPTUNE, having been overtaken by Uranus in 1993, is at opposition on July 14, at a distance of 4362 million kilometres (2710 million miles). Neptune is in Sagittarius. It is not visible to the naked eye, since its magnitude is at +7.9.

SIZES OF THE PLANETS. Uranus and Neptune are still close together in the sky. Neptune is more than two magnitudes the fainter of the two, but this is because of its greater distance; in size the two planets are virtual twins – though Neptune is considerably the more massive.

It used to be thought that Neptune was slightly larger than Uranus; in fact, it is very slightly smaller. It was also thought that Pluto might be at least as large as the Earth, whereas it is actually smaller than the Moon. It may therefore be useful to give the latest values for the diameters of the chief members of the Solar System:

Planet	Equatorial diameter (in miles)	Object	Longest diameter (in miles)
Mercury	3032	Ganymede	3274
Venus	7523	Titan	3201
Earth	7927	Callisto	2987
Mars	4222	Io	2275
Jupiter	89,424	Moon	2160
Saturn	74,914	Europa	1945
Uranus	31,770	Triton	1681
Neptune	31,410	Titania	981
Pluto	1444	Rhea	950
		Oberon	947
		Iapetus	892
		Charon	753
		Umbriel	727
		Ariel	720
		Dione	696
		Tethys	650
		Ceres	584

These are the only bodies over 500 miles in diameter. Only one asteroid is included (Ceres). Two satellites – Ganymede and Titan – are larger than Mercury, though much less massive; five satellites are larger than our Moon, and seven satellites are larger than Pluto. At the other end of the scale come Jupiter's tiny satellite Leda (estimated diameter 6 miles) and Deimos, the smaller attendant of Mars (longest diameter 9 miles). The smallest known asteroid seems to be 1991 BA, with an estimated diameter of 30 feet; asteroid 2340, Hathor, has a diameter of about one-third of a mile.

(On December 5, 1991 a strange object, given the asteroidal designation of 1991 VG, passed within 300,000 miles of the Earth. The estimated diameter was 20 feet. However, there is a doubt about its nature. It may be an asteroid, in which case it would be the smallest known, but there are also suggestions that it may have been a piece of space debris from an Earth-launched rocket.)

THIS MONTH'S CENTENARY. The Belgian cosmologist Georges Édouard Lemaître was born at Charleroi on July 17, 1894. He trained as a civil engineer, served during World War I with the Belgian Army, and then became a priest. He became acquainted with the leading cosmologists of the time – notably Arthur Eddington, Harlow Shapley, and Edwin Hubble – and it was he who first proposed the concept of the 'Big Bang', when the entire Universe came into being at one set moment. From 1927 he was Professor of Astrophysics at the University of Louvain, and was active in popularizing cosmological theories as well as undertaking theoretical research.

According to Lemaître, the Big Bang occurred between 20,000 million and 60,000 million years ago. The Universe was created as a single 'primæval atom', which exploded and sent material outward in all directions. There was a sort of tug-of-war between the opposing forces of expansion and contraction; eventually expansion won, and for the last 9000 million years the galaxies have been moving away from each other. Of course Lemaître's original theory has been modified, but in essence it is very similar to the modern view.

AUGUST

New Moon: August 7   *Full Moon:* August 21

MERCURY passes through superior conjunction on August 13, and will not be visible to observers in the British Isles. Further south it will become visible as an evening object towards the end of the month, low on the western horizon, shortly after sunset. Its magnitude is about −0.7. See the diagram given with the notes for September.

VENUS reaches greatest eastern elongation (46°) on August 24, with a magnitude of −4.6, and is thus a magnificent object in the western sky after sunset. The visibility conditions are quite different in the two hemispheres: whereas observers in latitude N.52° will only see the planet for an hour after sunset, those in latitude S.35° will find that Venus is setting over 3½ hours after sunset. Venus passes less than 1° south of Spica on the evening of July 31.

MARS, magnitude +1.2, continues to be visible as a morning object, moving steadily from Taurus to Gemini during the month.

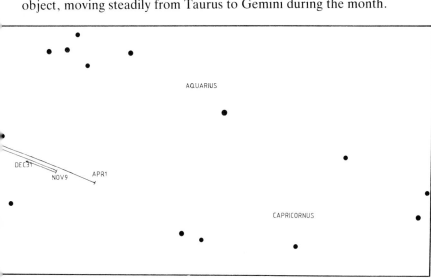

Figure 6. The path of Saturn.

JUPITER, magnitude −1.9, is a bright evening object, passing from Virgo into Libra early in the month.

SATURN continues to be visible for the greater part of the night as it approaches opposition. Its magnitude is +0.6. The rings are now noticeably thinner than in the last few years. The polar diameter of Saturn is 17″ while the minor axis of the rings is only 5″. Figure 6 shows the path of Saturn amongst the stars during 1994.

PERSEUS. This is the month of the Perseid meteors, and in 1994 the Moon will not interfere to any great extent. We may therefore expect a good display; the Perseids, unlike the November Leonids, are very reliable.

Perseus is a very prominent northern constellation. Its leader, Mirphak, lies at declination +50°, and is therefore inconveniently low from countries such as South Africa and Australia, while from part of New Zealand it never rises at all. During August it is best seen in the early hours of the morning.

The leading stars are as follows:

	Star	Magnitude	Spectrum	Luminosity (Sun = 1)	Distance light-years
α	Mirphak	1.80	F5	6000	620
β	Algol	2.12 (max.)	B8	100	95
ζ	Atik	2.85	B1	15,000	1108
ε		2.89	B0.5	2700	680
γ		2.93	G8	67	110
δ		3.01	B5	650	325
ϱ	Gorgonea Terti	3.2 (max.)	M4	130	195
η	Miram	3.76	K3	4500	815
ι		3.77	F5	520	450
κ	Misam	3.80	K0	75	170
o	Ati	3.83	B1	4500	1000
σ	Kerb	3.95	G4	67	175
υ	Nembus	4.04	B3	400	450

Perseus is easy enough to find. It is a rich area, as it is crossed by the Milky Way, and it contains some interesting objects. The most celebrated of these is the eclipsing binary Algol, which has a range

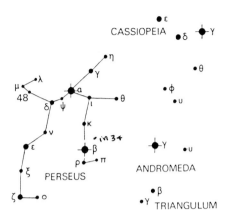

Figure 7. The northern constellation Perseus.

of magnitude from 2.1 to 3.4 and a period of 2.87 days. Minima are listed in the British periodical *Astronomy Now*, and are fascinating to watch; minimum brightness lasts for only twenty minutes.

Rho Persei is a red semi-regular variable with a very rough period of between 35 and 55 days; Kappa makes a good comparison star. Eta, Theta, Gamma, Zeta, and Epsilon are all easy doubles, and there are two Messier objects, the open cluster M.34 and the planetary nebula M.76. M.34 is on the fringe of naked-eye visibility, but M.76 is reputedly the faintest of all the objects in Messier's catalogue. It is nicknamed the 'Little Dumb-bell', and the integrated magnitude is below 12, while the central star is only of magnitude 16.6; the star is however very hot, with a surface temperature of around 60,000° Centigrade.

PLANETARY NEBULÆ are ill-named, because they are not truly nebulæ and have nothing whatsoever to do with planets! A planetary nebula is an old star which has shed its outer layers. No doubt our Sun will become a planetary nebula in the far future. The best-known member of the class is the Ring Nebula, M.57, in Lyra between the stars Beta and Gamma Lyræ; M.27, in Vulpecula, is known as the 'Dumb-bell' because of its appearance.

A very interesting observation has been made with the Hubble Space Telescope, now orbiting the Earth at a height of 300 miles. This concerns Hen 1357, so named because it is the 1357th object in a catalogue compiled by Karl Henize. A few decades ago, Hen 1357 was an ordinary hot star; now it has started to look like a planetary nebula – Hubble has 'caught it in the act', so to speak. It is 18,000 light-years away.

This is yet another proof that despite the fault in the original mirror, the Hubble Telescope has been a great success; in many ways it could out-perform any ground-based telescope even before the attempt to install a corrective lens to compensate for the fault. It is a pioneering instrument, and as such it will always be remembered.

SEPTEMBER

New Moon: September 5   *Full Moon:* September 19

Equinox: September 23

MERCURY attains its greatest eastern elongation (26°) on September 26, and is therefore an evening object, though not for observers in northern temperate latitudes. For observers in southern latitudes this will be the most favourable evening apparition of the year. Figure 8 shows, for observers in latitude S.35°, the changes in azimuth (true bearing from the north through east, south, and west) and altitude of Mercury on successive evenings when the Sun is 6° below the horizon. This condition is known as the end of evening civil twilight, and in this latitude and at this time of year occurs about 30 minutes after sunset. The changes in the brightness of the planet are indicated by the relative sizes of the circles marking Mercury's position at five-day intervals. It will be noticed that Mercury is at its brightest before it reaches greatest eastern elongation (26°) on September 26. There is little variation in the magnitude of Mercury throughout September, being −0.4 at the beginning and +0.2 at the end.

VENUS, magnitude −4.6, continues to be visible as a magnificent object in the western evening sky. Sadly, for observers in northern temperate latitudes, the increase in its southern declination means that, for them, Venus is too close to the Sun for observation before the end of the month. In particular, observers in the British Isles are unlikely to glimpse it after the middle of September.

MARS is still a morning object, magnitude +1.1. By the end of the month observers in the British Isles may be able to detect it low above the east-north-east horizon by midnight. Mars is in Gemini at the beginning of September, passing south of Castor and Pollux during the second half of the month.

JUPITER, magnitude −1.8, is a bright evening object in Libra, visible in the western sky after sunset. For observers in northern temperate latitudes Jupiter is coming to the end of its evening apparition and for those in the latitudes of the British Isles it will be lost to view in the evening twilight before the end of the month.

SATURN, magnitude +0.5, is at opposition on September 1 and is thus visible throughout the hours of darkness. At closest approach Saturn is 1302 million kilometres (809 million miles) from the Earth.

Iapetus. Saturn is at opposition this month. The rings are now closing as seen from Earth, and in 1995 will be edgewise-on. Temporarily Saturn will lose its beauty, but edgewise presentations provide excellent opportunities for observing the satellites. Of these only one, Titan, is really large. Next in order come Rhea and Iapetus, and Iapetus has points of special interest.

It was discovered by G. D. Cassini in 1671. Cassini soon noticed that it is very variable, and is much brighter when west of Saturn than when to the east of the planet. Cassini even stated that near eastern elongation, Iapetus disappears altogether. Of course this is

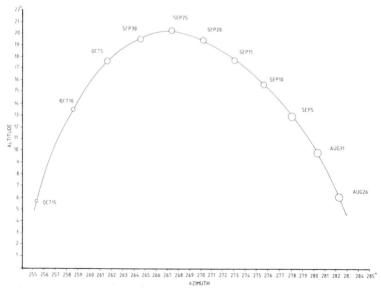

Figure 8. Evening apparition of Mercury for latitude S.35°.

not true, but the magnitude falls to below 12, whereas at western elongation it can exceed 10.

It was assumed – correctly, as we now know – that the rotation is synchronous; that is to say, Iapetus spins on its axis in the same time that it takes to complete one orbit – over 79 Earth days; it is well over a million miles from Saturn. If the two hemispheres have unequal reflecting power, and we see the more reflective area at every western elongation, the changes in brightness can be explained.

This was confirmed by the Voyager space-craft, which obtained good images of Iapetus. The leading hemisphere is as black as a blackboard, with an albedo of from 0.04 to 0.05, while the trailing hemisphere has an albedo as high as 0.5! The line of demarcation is not sharp: there is a 150-mile transition zone. Both bright and dark regions are cratered; some of the craters in the bright area have dark floors.

Iapetus is of low density, so it seems certain that the globe is a mixture of rock and ice, and that the dark surface represents a deposit of some kind. Carl Sagan has suggested that it may be thick, and made up of organics; others believe that it may be a mere surface stain. A suggestion that it may be due to material wafted on to Iapetus from the outermost satellite, Phœbe, has now been abandoned, partly because the characteristics of the Iapetus stain and the surface of Phœbe are different and partly because Phœbe seems to be too small and too far away (it has retrograde motion, and is almost certainly an ex-asteroid). Further information about the Iapetus puzzle must presumably await results from the next space-probe.

HR Delphini. In 1967 G. E. D. Alcock discovered a nova in Delphinus, the Dolphin – a small but very distinctive constellation in the region of Cygnus and Aquila; it looks almost like a star-cluster, and unwary observers have even been known to mistake it for the Pleiades! The nova, now known as HR Delphini, rose to magnitude 3.7. It behaved in a very unusual way, and remained visible to the naked eye for months before starting a slow decline. The pre-outburst magnitude was 12.7; the present brightness is about the same, and it is not very likely that the nova will fade much more. Whether there will be another outburst remains to be seen, but amateur observers will do well to keep watch on it. The position (epoch 2000) is: RA $20^h 42^m.3$, dec. $+19°10'$.

OCTOBER

Summer Time in Great Britain and Northern Ireland ends on October 23.

MERCURY, for observers in equatorial and southern latitudes, continues to be visible as an evening object for the first half of the month, and observers should refer to Figure 8 given with the notes for September. Mercury passes rapidly through inferior conjunction on October 21 and for the last few days of the month will be visible as a morning object low in the east before sunrise. Its magnitude brightens rapidly during these few days, reaching +0.3 on October 31.

VENUS is no longer visible to observers in northern temperate latitudes. However, for those in the Southern Hemisphere Venus continues to be visible as a magnificent object, magnitude −4.6, dominating the western sky after sunset, though by the end of the month it is getting too close to the Sun for observation.

MARS, magnitude +0.9, is a morning object though observers in northern temperate latitudes should be able to detect it low above the east-north-eastern horizon before midnight. Mars is in Cancer, and passes just south of the Beehive cluster around October 17.

JUPITER, magnitude −1.7, is still an evening object for observers in equatorial and southern latitudes, but only visible for a short while after sunset, low in the western sky.

SATURN is now an evening object, magnitude +0.6.

THE TAURID METEORS. At the present time the Taurids do not compare with other spectacular showers – but there are suggestions that things may have been very different in the past.

The shower begins around October 20, and ends around November 30. Apparently there are two branches – the Northern Taurids and the Southern Taurids – and the maxima are very ill-defined; the ZHR or Zenithal Hourly Rate is not usually above 10. (The ZHR is the number of meteors which would be expected to be seen with the naked eye by an observer under perfect conditions, with the radiant at the zenith. In practice these conditions are never fulfilled, so that the observed rate is always rather less than the theoretical ZHR.) Yet in 1968 I. S. Astapovich and A. K. Terenteva carried out a study of fireballs seen during the period between the first and fifteenth centuries, and concluded that the Taurids were then pre-eminent; 'the post powerful shower of the year in the 11th century, with 42 fireballs belonging to them, and no shower, not even the great ones, could be compared with them as to activity'. The modern streams were identified only in 1869, by G. Zezioli and T. W. Backhouse.

In 1950 F. L. Whipple and S. Hamid investigated the origin of the Taurids, and concluded that 'the Taurid streams were formed chiefly by a violent ejection of material from Encke's Comet some 4700 years ago, but also by another ejection some 1500 years ago, from a body moving in an orbit of similar shape and longitude of perihelion but somewhat greater aphelion distance'. It was also suggested that this second body had earlier separated from Encke's Comet.

Based on these and other results, V. Clube and W. Napier have proposed that the Taurids were brilliant in ancient times, and that they have been responsible for some of the old legends about spectacular phenomena in the sky. In any case, there seems no doubt that Encke's Comet is the parent of the stream.

PRÆSEPE. In mid-October Mars, now becoming fairly bright, passes through Cancer close to M.44, the 'Beehive' cluster more generally known as Præsepe. This is one of the most famous clusters in the sky, and is a very easy naked-eye object.

It has been known since very ancient times. Aratus, around 250 BC, wrote that if the cluster were invisible in an apparently cloudless sky, rain was sure to be on the way. In 130 BC Hipparchus listed it as 'a cloudy star'. It is flanked by two stars, Delta Cancri (magnitude 3.9) and Gamma Cancri (4.7) which are known as the Aselli or Asses, since another name for Præsepe is 'the Manger'; and in 1610 Galileo, using his newly made telescope, commented that the cluster 'contains not one star only, but a mass of more than 40 small stars . . . I have counted 36 besides the Aselli'.

Præsepe is clearly older than the Pleiades. It contains no nebulosity, and many of its stars are reddish or orange, indicating that they have left the Main Sequence. The distance has been given as 525 light-years. The diameter is 70 arc-minutes, so that the best views are obtained with binoculars or wide-field telescopes; the conjunction with Mars this month provides an interesting target for astronomical photographers.

NOVEMBER

New Moon: November 3 *Full Moon:* November 18

MERCURY reaches greatest western elongation (19°) on November 6. For observers in northern temperate latitudes this will be the most favourable morning apparition of the year. Figure 9 shows, for observers in latitutde N.52°, the changes in azimuth (true bearing from the north through east, south, and west) and altitude of Mercury on successive mornings when the Sun is 6° below the horizon. This condition is known as the beginning of morning civil twilight, and in this latitude and at this time of year occurs about 35 minutes before sunrise. The changes in the brightness of the planet are indicated by the relative sizes of the circles marking Mercury's position at five-day intervals. It will be noticed that Mercury is at its brightest after it reaches greatest western elongation (19°) on November 6. In fact its magnitude brightens from +0.1 at the beginning of the month to −0.8 on November 19. Mercury is unsuitably placed for observation by those in the Southern Hemisphere.

VENUS is not visible at first, as it passes through inferior conjunction on November 2. It moves rapidly away from the Sun and by the middle of the month has become visible low above the southeastern horizon before sunrise. Venus has a magnitude of −4.6. Around November 14 Venus and Mercury are equidistant from the Sun, Venus being about 5° south of Mercury.

MARS is starting to increase in brightness at last as it moves towards opposition (February 1995), its magnitude increasing during the month from +0.7 to +0.3. Mars moves from Cancer into Leo early in November.

JUPITER might just be glimpsed for the first few days of the month as an evening object, to observers in equatorial latitudes, but thereafter it is too close to the Sun for observation, passing through conjunction on November 17.

SATURN, magnitude +0.8, continues to be visible as an evening object, though no longer visible to observers in the British Isles after midnight.

A MARTIAN ANNIVERSARY. Twenty years ago, on November 28, 1964, Mariner 4 was launched towards Mars. It reached the neighbourhood of the Red Planet on the following July 14, at a minimum distance of 6084 miles, and sent back 21 images. It more than compensated for the failure of its twin, Mariner 3, which had been launched on November 5, 1964, but had gone out of control almost immediately, so that contact was lost and was never regained.

Before the flight of Mariner 4 there was still a great deal about Mars that we did not know. In particular, it was widely believed that the polar caps were no more than very thin deposits, possibly of solid carbon dioxide. The surface was believed to be smooth, or at most gently undulating, with no high peaks or deep valleys; the atmospheric pressure was given as around 87 millibars, and the main constituent was thought to be nitrogen. Most important of all, the dark areas were often taken to be old sea-beds filled with organic matter – 'vegetation', in fact.

Mariner 4 caused a dramatic change in outlook. The polar caps are thick, and a mixture of carbon dioxide ice and water ice; the surface is cratered; the atmospheric pressure is below 10 millibars everywhere, and the main constituent is carbon dioxide. The dark

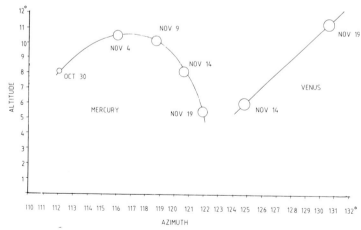

Figure 9. Morning apparition of Mercury for latitude N.52°.

areas are not depressions (the most prominent of them, the V-shaped Syrtis Major, is an elevated plateau) and there is no vegetation; the dark areas are nothing more than albedo features.

Mariner 4 also gave the *coup de grâce* to the idea of canals on Mars. In the 1950s many astronomers, including the foremost authority on Mars – Gérard de Vaucouleurs – were still maintaining that the canals had 'a basis of reality', but in the Mariner 4 images they were conspicuous only by their absence.

Really detailed views, showing the great volcanoes, had to wait for the mission of Mariner 9, in 1971; but it was Mariner 4 which provided the basis for modern thinking about Mars. Contact with it was finally lost on December 20, 1967; doubtless it is still orbiting the Sun.

THIS MONTH'S CENTENARY. The Dutch astronomer Herman Zanstra was born at Heerenveen, in Friesland, on November 3, 1894. He was educated in Amsterdam, and carried out research in London and the USA before becoming Radcliffe Travelling Fellow of the University of Oxford and observer at the new Radcliffe Observatory at Pretoria, in South Africa. He was concerned largely with the spectra of comets, and in 1930 carried out pioneer investigations into the temperatures of the central stars of planetary nebulæ.

BORRELLY'S COMET. This comet, with a period of 7 years, reaches perihelion this month, but will certainly not be bright: indeed it has never equalled its magnitude at the time of its discovery in 1889 – the magnitude was then 8. It has been calculated that in 1886 the comet made a close approach to Jupiter (0.001 astronomical units) and spent two days inside the satellite system, closer to Jupiter than the orbit of Io. Some disruption was noted in 1889, but at least the comet survived.

DECEMBER

New Moon: December 2   *Full Moon:* December 18

Solstice: December 22

MERCURY passes slowly through superior conjunction on December 14 and is unsuitably placed for observation throughout the month.

VENUS is a brilliant object, attaining greatest brilliancy (magnitude −4.6) on December 9. It dominates the south-eastern sky for several hours before dawn. Have you ever seen Venus in daylight? A good opportunity for doing so occurs on the morning of December 29, when observers could use the old crescent Moon as a guide. The Moon passes 3° south of Venus at about 04ʰ GMT on that day (remember that the Moon moves at an angular speed roughly equivalent to its own diameter every hour).

MARS, its magnitude brightening from +0.3 to −0.3 during the month, is now visible from the late evening onwards. As will be seen from Figure 5, given with the notes for June, Mars is in Leo, passing north of the first magnitude star Regulus on December 8. Mars is a whole magnitude brighter than Regulus.

JUPITER is too close to the Sun for observation at the beginning of the month. It then emerges from the morning twilight and becomes visible low in the south-eastern sky, magnitude −1.8. Observers in the British Isles should be able to see it after the first ten days of December.

SATURN, magnitude +1.0, is an evening object in Aquarius, in the south-western quadrant of the sky.

PIONEERS TO JUPITER. It is now twenty years since the space-probe Pioneer 11 by-passed Jupiter; it did so on December 2, 1974, at a range of 28,838 miles. Its predecessor, Pioneer 10, had passed the Giant Planet on December 3, 1973, at 81,666 miles.

These were the first space-craft to reach the outer Solar System. There had been misgivings about the crossing of the asteroid belt; the large asteroids could be allowed for, but nobody was sure about the numbers of smaller bodies – and a collision between a Pioneer and an object the size of a tennis-ball would have disastrous consequences. However, the Pioneers escaped unscathed, and so have all the subsequent probes to have crossed the asteroid zone (Voyagers 1 and 2, Galileo, and Ulysses), so that evidently the danger is not so great as had been feared – unless, of course, we have been exceptionally lucky!

Both Pioneers were completely successful, and sent back excellent images as well as data of all kinds. Pioneer 11 even went on to a rendezvous with Saturn, on September 1, 1979. Each space-craft carries a plaque, which is intended to show any aliens who may collect the probes just where they came from – though whether any aliens would be able to decipher the messages on the plaques is somewhat debatable.

The Pioneers are now on their way out of the Solar System. Contact with them is still maintained, but in a few years we are bound to lose track of them, and their final fate will never be known. Certainly they have honoured places in astronomical history; it is perhaps unfortunate that in the future they will be largely forgotten, simply because their achievements were overshadowed by those of the Voyagers between 1979 and 1989.

THE COLOUR OF ACHERNAR. As seen from countries such as South Africa, Australia, and New Zealand, Achernar (Alpha Eridani) is now near the zenith (as it lies at declination −57°, it can never be seen from Britain or Europe). It is the ninth brightest star in the sky. The spectrum is B5; it is 780 times as luminous as the Sun, and 85 light-years away. It is white, or slightly blueish. Yet in Chambers' catalogue of red stars, published during the last century, it is given as 'red', and there are several other similar reports.

There is not the slightest chance that there has been any change in Achernar in historic times, so that its classification as red is completely wrong. It tends to lessen one's faith in the idea of any change in Sirius, which was described as red by some ancient observers and is now pure white!

VENUS IN THE EAST. Venus is now at its best, in the east before dawn – and there are bound to be the usual inquiries about any possible connection with the Star of Bethlehem. This has been discussed in previous *Yearbooks*, and all that need be said here is that the Star of Bethlehem was nothing commonplace – which rules out Venus or any other planet; we can also discard the various other theories, such as planetary conjunctions, novæ and supernovæ (these would have been noted in the records of the time). In investigating the Star of Bethlehem we have nothing to guide us apart from one reference in the Bible, and it is unlikely that the problem will ever be solved now.

Eclipses in 1994

During 1994 there will be three eclipses, two of the Sun and one of the Moon.

1. *An annular eclipse of the Sun on May 10* is visible as a partial eclipse from the eastern Pacific including Hawaii, northern Siberia, North and Central America and also the extreme northern edge of Colombia and Venezuela, the West Indies, the Atlantic Ocean, the Arctic Ocean, Greenland, Iceland, western Europe (including the British Isles), and north-west and west Africa. The eclipse begins at 14^h 12^m and ends at 20^h 11^m. The track of the annular phase crosses North America from Lower California to Nova Scotia and then crosses the North Atlantic to Morocco. The annular phase begins at 15^h 21^m and ends at 19^h 02^m. The maximum duration of the annular phase is 6^m 14^s.

At Greenwich the partial eclipse begins at 17^h 36^m and ends (at sunset) at 19^h 31^m.

At Edinburgh the partial eclipse begins at 17^h 31^m and ends at 19^h 25^m.

As seen from the British Isles approximately half of the Sun is obscured at maximum.

2. *A partial eclipse of the Moon on May 25* is visible from Europe (including the British Isles), the Atlantic Ocean, Africa, Madagascar, Iceland, southern Greenland, Antarctica, the Americas except the extreme north-west, and the Pacific Ocean. The eclipse begins at 02^h 37^m and ends at 04^h 23^m. For most of the British Isles except the extreme south-west of England and Wales, and also for Ireland, the Moon will have set before the eclipse ends.

3. *A total eclipse of the Sun on November 3* is visible as a partial eclipse from the eastern South Pacific Ocean, Central and South America, the Atlantic Ocean, part of Antarctica, southern Africa, and Madagascar. The eclipse begins at 11^h 05^m and ends at 16^h 13^m. The path of totality crosses southern Peru, southern Bolivia, Paraguay, and southern Brazil. The total phase begins at 12^h 02^m and ends at 15^h 16^m.

Occultations in 1994

In the course of its journey round the sky each month, the Moon passes in front of all the stars in its path, and the timing of these occultations is useful in fixing the position and motion of the Moon. The Moon's orbit is tilted at more than five degrees to the ecliptic, but it is not fixed in space. It twists steadily westwards at a rate of about twenty degrees a year, a complete revolution taking 18.6 years, during which time all the stars that lie within about six and a half degrees of the ecliptic will be occulted. The occultations of any one star continue month after month until the Moon's path has twisted away from the star but only a few of these occultations will be visible at any one place in hours of darkness.

There are six occultations of bright planets in 1994, one of Venus, one of Mars, and four of Jupiter.

Only four first-magnitude stars are near enough to the ecliptic to be occulted by the Moon; these are Regulus, Aldebaran, Spica, and Antares. Only Spica undergoes on occultation (14 times) in 1994.

Predictions of these occultations are made on a world-wide basis for all stars down to magnitude 7.5, and sometimes even fainter. The British Astronomical Association has just produced the first complete lunar occultation prediction package for microcomputer users.

Recently occultations of stars by planets (including minor planets) and satellites have aroused considerable attention.

The exact timing of such events gives valuable information about positions, sizes, orbits, atmospheres and sometimes of the presence of satellites. The discovery of the rings of Uranus in 1977 was the unexpected result of the observations made of a predicted occultation of a faint star by Uranus. The duration of an occultation by a satellite or minor planet is quite small (usually of the order of a minute or less). If observations are made from a number of stations it is possible to deduce the size of the planet.

The observations need to be made either photoelectrically or visually. The high accuracy of the method can readily be appreciated when one realizes that even a stop-watch timing accurate to $0^s.1$ is, on average, equivalent to an accuracy of about 1 kilometre in the chord measured across the minor planet.

Comets in 1994

The appearance of a bright comet is a rare event which can never be predicted in advance, because this class of object travels round the Sun in an enormous orbit with a period which may well be many thousands of years. There are therefore no records of the previous appearances of these bodies, and we are unable to follow their wanderings through space.

Comets of short period, on the other hand, return at regular intervals, and attract a good deal of attention from astronomers. Unfortunately they are all faint objects, and are recovered and followed by photographic methods using large telescopes. Most of these short-period comets travel in orbits of small inclination which reach out to the orbit of Jupiter, and it is this planet which is mainly responsible for the severe perturbations which many of these comets undergo. Unlike the planets, comets may be seen in any part of the sky, but since their distances from the Earth are similar to those of the planets their apparent movements in the sky are also somewhat similar, and some of them may be followed for long periods of time.

The following periodic comets are expected to return to perihelion in 1994, and to be brighter than magnitude +15.

Comet	Year of discovery	Period (years)	Predicted date of perihelion 1994
Encke	1785	3.3	Feb. 9
Tuttle	1790	13.5	June 26
Tempel (1)	1867	5.5	July 3
Wild (3)	1980	6.9	July 21
Borrelly	1905	6.9	Nov. 1

Minor Planets in 1994

Although many thousands of minor planets (asteroids) are known to exist, only 3,000 of these have well-determined orbits and are listed in the catalogues. Most of these orbits lie entirely between the orbits of Mars and Jupiter. All of these bodies are quite small, and even the largest, Ceres, is only about 960 kilometres in diameter. Thus, they are necessarily faint objects, and although a number of them are within the reach of a small telescope few of them ever reach any considerable brightness. The first four that were discovered are named Ceres, Pallas, Juno and Vesta. Actually the largest four minor planets are Ceres, Pallas, Vesta and Hygeia (excluding 2060 Chiron, which orbits mainly between the paths of Saturn and Uranus, and whose nature is uncertain). Vesta can occasionally be seen with the naked eye and this is most likely to occur when an opposition occurs near June, since Vesta would then be at perihelion. Approximate dates of opposition (and magnitude) for these minor planets in 1994 are: Pallas, November 8 ($8^m.0$), Juno, April 15 ($9^m.8$), and Vesta, December 25 ($6^m.3$).

A vigorous campaign for observing the occultations of stars by the minor planets has produced improved values for the dimensions of some of them, as well as the suggestion that some of these planets may be accompanied by satellites. Many of these observations have been made photoelectrically. However, amateur observers have found renewed interest in the minor planets since it has been shown that their visual timings of an occultation of a star by a minor planet are accurate enough to lead to reliable determinations of diameter. As a consequence many groups of observers all over the world are now organizing themselves for expeditions should the predicted track of such an occultation cross their country.

In 1984 the British Astronomical Association formed a special Asteroid and Remote Planets Section.

Meteors in 1994

Meteors ('shooting stars') may be seen on any clear moonless night, but on certain nights of the year their number increases noticeably. This occurs when the Earth chances to intersect a concentration of meteoric dust moving in an orbit around the Sun. If the dust is well spread out in space, the resulting shower of meteors may last for several days. The word 'shower' must not be misinterpreted – only on very rare occasions have the meteors been so numerous as to resemble snowflakes falling.

If the meteor tracks are marked on a star map and traced backwards, a number of them will be found to intersect in a point (or a small area of the sky) which marks the radiant of the shower. This gives the direction from which the meteors have come.

The following table gives some of the more easily observed showers with their radiants; interference by moonlight is shown by the letter M.

Limiting dates	Shower	Maximum	R.A. Dec.	
Jan. 1–4	Quadrantids	Jan. 4	$15^h28^m + 50°$	M
April 20–22	Lyrids	April 21	$18^h08^m + 32°$	M
May 1–8	Aquarids	May 5	$22^h20^m + 00°$	
June 17–26	Ophiuchids	June 20	$17^h20^m - 20°$	M
July 15–Aug. 15	Delta Aquarids	July 29	$22^h36^m - 17°$	
July 15–Aug. 20	Piscis Australids	July 31	$22^h40^m - 30°$	M
July 15–Aug. 25	Capricornids	Aug. 2	$20^h36^m - 10°$	M
July 27–Aug. 17	Perseids	Aug. 12	$3^h04^m + 58°$	
Oct. 15–25	Orionids	Oct. 22	$6^h24^m + 15°$	M
Oct. 26–Nov. 16	Taurids	Nov. 3	$3^h44^m + 14°$	
Nov. 15–19	Leonids	Nov. 17	$10^h08^m + 22°$	M
Dec. 9–14	Geminids	Dec. 13	$7^h28^m + 32°$	M
Dec. 17–24	Ursids	Dec. 23	$14^h28^m + 78°$	M

M = moonlight interferes

Some Events in 1995

ECLIPSES

There will be three eclipses, two of the Sun and one of the Moon.

April 15: partial eclipse of the Moon – America, Australasia, Asia.

April 29: annular eclipse of the Sun – America (not North), West Africa.

October 24: total eclipse of the Sun – Arabia, Asia, Australia.

THE PLANETS

Mercury may be seen more easily from northern latitudes in the evenings about the time of greatest eastern elongation (May 12) and in the mornings around greatest western elongation (October 20). In the Southern Hemisphere the dates are March 1 (morning) and September 9 (evening).

Venus is visible in the mornings until July. From October onwards it is visible in the evenings.

Mars is at opposition on February 12.

Jupiter is at opposition on June 1.

Saturn is at opposition on September 14.

Uranus is at opposition on July 21.

Neptune is at opposition on July 17.

Pluto is at opposition on May 20.

Slow Moving Object 1992 QB1

DAVID JEWITT

Oort's Cloud and Kuiper's Belt

Astronomers have long realized that the observable comets must be new arrivals in the inner Solar System. An active comet like P/Halley loses about 0.01% of its total mass per orbit. Thus, cometary lifetimes in the inner Solar System are measured in tens of thousands of orbits, corresponding to periods of hundreds of thousands of years. Comets may be deflected out of the Solar System on even shorter timescales. In the 4.5 *billion* years since the formation of the Solar System, all comets that are now active would have long ago lost their volatiles, leaving behind either inactive, asteroid-like nuclei, or streams of dust like those now observed in the meteor streams. Comets may have formed in the earliest days of the Solar System, but they have been stored in 'deep freeze' until recent times.

The best-known storage location for the comets is Oort's Cloud, proposed in 1950 by the Dutch astronomer Jan Oort. The Oort Cloud is a spherical system containing about 10^{12} comets, and having a diameter of about 100,000 AU, or roughly 0.5 parsecs. In Oort's model, the outer comets in the cloud are strongly susceptible to the gravitational perturbations of passing stars. Close passes by stars gradually deflect the orbits of comets so that they dip into the planetary region, where their nuclei may be heated by the Sun, leading to sublimation of the ices and the production of the familiar cometary coma and tails.

For most of the past forty years, Oort's hypothesis has seemed to account for the known orbital properties of comets with extraordinary accuracy. The model explains the observed concentration of cometary orbits with semi-major axes ~50,000 AU. The Long Period Comets (LPCs; orbit periods >200 years) are observed to fall into the planetary region from random directions, as would be expected for comets originating in a spherical cloud. However, Oort's model applies specifically to the Long Period Comets. The commonly observed Short Period Comets (SPCs) were supposed to be derived from the LPCs via gravitational capture by the planets, primarily Jupiter.

Doubts about the efficiency of cometary capture by Jupiter were raised in the 1970s by Paul Joss. He noted that the probability of capture was so small that the known number of SPCs could not be explained. However, because of computational limitations, researchers were unable to prove this result, and Oort's Cloud remained as the accepted source of comets, long period and short period alike.

An alternative source was suggested by a group of Canadian astronomers in 1988, based on more advanced computer simulations of the process of capture by the gas giant planets. In agreement with Joss, they too found that the efficiency of capture was small, but also noted that capture of comets from the spherical Oort Cloud would tend to produce a *spherical* swarm of short period comets. In contrast, the orbits of SPCs are concentrated near the plane of the Solar System, with mean inclinations of about 30 degrees. Duncan, Quinn and Tremaine (DQT) proposed instead that the SPCs are captured from a flattened distribution of original orbits, perhaps a sheet of comets in the outer Solar System. The small inclinations of the SPCs would then reflect the small inclinations of comets in this new cometary source.

The idea of a sheet or ring of comets in the outer Solar System is an old one. It was discussed in some detail in a long review paper by Gerard Kuiper in 1951, a year after Oort's suggestion of the more distant, spherical cloud. Kuiper and others reasoned that the Solar System should not end abruptly at Neptune or Pluto, and envisioned the 'belt' as consisting of residual material left over from the formation of the Solar System. The density of matter in the outer regions would be so low that large planets would not have grown there. Smaller objects, perhaps of asteroidal dimensions, might exist. Because of the low temperatures, it seemed likely that these distant objects would be ice-rich, making them very similar if not identical to the nuclei of comets.

The so-called 'Kuiper Belt' hypothesis was not beyond question, however. In order to make their calculation tractable, DQT artificially multiplied the masses of the outer planets by factors 10 to 40, thereby increasing the force of gravity and speeding up the orbital evolution of comets during capture. Mark Bailey and collaborators in England worried that this computational device might lead to spurious results, and questioned the results of DQT.

Slow Moving Objects and 1992 QB1

Why is the outer Solar System empty? Apart from Pluto, there are no known objects with orbits outside the gas giant planets. True, some comets (including Halley's) move on eccentric orbits that reach large distances, but in general the emptiness of the outer Solar System is startling compared to the rich abundance of small bodies inside the orbit of Jupiter. These include hundreds of short period comets and near-Earth asteroids, as well as thousands of asteroids in the belt between Mars and Jupiter (more than 5000 asteroids have been numbered).

There are at least two plausible answers to the above question. First, the outer Solar System might be truly empty because the orbits of distant objects are unstable to perturbations by the gas giant planets. In this case, any objects that were originally present in the outer Solar System would have been removed, either by ejection to the stars, or by injection to the inner Solar System. Second, it is possible that the absence of objects is purely an artifact of observational selection. Because distant objects are far from the Sun, they will necessarily be faint, and therefore difficult to detect.

In 1987, Dr Jane Luu (now at the University of California at Berkeley) and I started a telescopic survey that was intended to provide an answer to the question 'Why is the outer Solar System empty?' Although our initial efforts employed photographic plates on a Schmidt telescope in Arizona, we soon decided that more interesting results would come from the application of charge coupled device (CCD) detectors on larger telescopes. CCDs are about 100 times more sensitive than photographic plates. Distant comets would be faint. Comet Halley, if removed to 50 AU, would fall beyond the limits of current technology at magnitude 30. Therefore, only larger objects could be detected by reflected light. But larger objects are rare, so that the search must be directed towards the detection of a relatively small number of large objects spread over a huge area of sky. CCDs cover a small area of sky, however, so that many fields must be observed with a CCD in order to gain results of significance. Partly because we started our work before the Kuiper Belt was made fashionable by Duncan and collaborators, and partly because we wanted a name that did not pre-judge the nature of distant objects, we referred to our work as a survey for Slow Moving Objects (SMOs).

The bulk of our SMO survey was conducted using the University of Hawaii's 2.2-m telescope on Mauna Kea, Hawaii. This telescope is of uncommonly good optical quality, allowing it to benefit from the fine seeing present atop Mauna Kea. The telescope is also equipped with a number of first-rate charge coupled device (CCD) cameras. For our survey, we chose the CCD with the largest number of pixels, a 2048 × 2048 device made by Tektronix. One last advantage is that the Tektronix CCD has an anti-reflection coating that acts to maximize its efficiency. At red wavelengths (about 7000 Å) the quantum efficiency is 90 per cent, meaning that 9 out of 10 photons hitting the CCD are actually recorded. This high quantum efficiency is unbeaten among astronomical CCDs; indeed, it is

UT 1992 Aug 30d 10h 56m

UT 1992 Aug 30d 13h 00m

N

Figure 1. CCD images from the UH 2.2-m telescope, showing two of the discovery images of 1992 QB1 (marked with arrows). Most other objects in the field are distant galaxies. The linear object at the north-east of the top image, and the south-west of the lower, is a main-belt asteroid. Its rapid motion across the CCD is in stark contrast to the crawl of QB1, emphasizing the extreme distance of the latter.

nearly perfect. Together, the fine seeing and the high quantum efficiency of the CCD allow us to surpass the performance of 4-m telescopes at poorer sites.

The CCD is used to take 4 consecutive images, each with an exposure of 900 seconds. The individual images reach to about magnitude 25. The four images are recorded over a period of two or more hours. A computer is used to compare the images to look for moving objects. On August 30, 1993, Jane and I were taking the third of a 4-image sequence while 'blinking' the first two images on a computer in the control room of the UH telescope. We noticed that an image of a 23rd magnitude 'star' appeared to move slightly between the successive images. The motion was only about 1/2 arcsecond, but it seemed real. When we compared the first two images with the third, we realized that we had indeed chanced upon an SMO (see Figure 1). The rate of motion – about 2.8 arcsecs per hour – suggested a distance of roughly 50 AU, placing the new object far beyond the present distances of Neptune or Pluto (both are near 30 AU).

We observed the SMO again on the following two nights, and obtained accurate astrometry and photometry every night. Each night we communicated our measurements to Brian Marsden of the Center for Astrophysics in Cambridge, Massachusetts. He confirmed that the SMO was at a vast distance, and assigned it the formal (though somewhat daunting) name 1992 QB1. Our photometry at three optical wavelengths suggested that QB1 was very red compared to the Sun. This kind of redness had been previously measured only in one planetary object – the peculiar asteroid/comet 5145 Pholus – and was there attributed to the presence of dark red organic (carbon-rich) material of a primitive nature. This heightened our excitement by suggesting that QB1 was similarly coated in red, organic matter. From the photometry, we also estimated the diameter of QB1 to be in the 200 km to 250 km range, about twenty times the diameter of the nucleus of comet Halley. So, by September 2 we knew that we had discovered an object beyond Pluto, that its surface was very red and might be coated with primitive organic matter, and that it was roughly 200 km in diameter. Unfortunately, the timebase of the discovery observations was too short to determine the shape of the orbit.

Since then, we and other astronomers have re-observed QB1 to refine the parameters of its orbit. The results are listed in Table 1 on page 124.

TABLE 1

Approximate Orbital Parameters[1]

Semi-major Axis	*a*	44.4 AU
Eccentricity	*e*	0.11
Inclination	*i*	2.2°
Orbital Period	*P*	296 years
Perihelion Date	*T*	2023 AD
Perihelion Distance	*q*	39.6 AU
Aphelion Distance	*Q*	49.1 AU

[1]Based on astrometry in the interval 1992 August 30–December 25. Orbit solution is by Brian Marsden (1992).

To our great delight, it appears from Table 1 that 1992 QB1 is probably a *bona fide* member of the Kuiper Belt. Its 40 AU perihelion distance prevents QB1 from crossing the orbit of Neptune (Neptune's aphelion is at 30 AU), so that close encounters and strong gravitational perturbations are not likely. While the dynamics of Kuiper Belt type orbits are poorly understood, it is probable that QB1 lies near the inner edge of a sheet of orbits that are stable over the age of the Solar System.

We suspect that QB1 is simply one of the brighter, larger members of the Kuiper Belt, and that its discovery signifies the presence of an enormous number of other objects awaiting detection. For instance, QB1 was detected in a survey of less than 1 square degree of sky. The area of the Kuiper Belt as seen from Earth is approximately 10,000 square degrees. Therefore, unless QB1 was a 1/10,000 chance discovery, there must be 10,000 similar objects awaiting detection, together with a much larger number of smaller, fainter bodies. The combined mass of 10,000 ice spheres each 200 km in diameter is about twice the mass of Pluto, or 0.2 per cent of the mass of the Earth.

We are continuing with our efforts to identify additional examples of SMOs. Other astronomers are expanding their efforts to understand the long-term dynamics of bodies beyond the planets. These parallel observational and theoretical efforts promise to open a new field of investigation, and remind us that even the contents of our own Solar System are not well known.

Since this article was written, two more SMOs have been found which appear to be of the same type: 1993 FW (discovered by Jewitt and Luu) and 1993 HA$_2$ (discovered by D. Rabinowitz). This supports the author's suggestion that objects from the Kuiper Belt are probably very numerous. – EDITOR

What lurks at the centre of our Galaxy?

DAVID ALLEN

Do you daydream of places you might one day visit? Do those distant, exotic spots on the globe beckon? Many years ago I set up my wish list: Easter Island, Antarctica, the Galapagos . . . The list has grown faster than I can tick them off, for the terrible thing about wanderlust is its narcotic nature.

But I am not writing about my travel aspirations. Well, not quite. You see, there are times when my mind drifts further afield. To the impossible. Sometimes I visualize myself clambering up Olympus Mons, that mighty volcano on Mars, to gaze into its giant summit caldera. On other occasions I am timing the fall of a pebble dropped from the towering cliff on Uranus's remarkable satellite Miranda. Calculations indicate that it would take five minutes to reach the bottom. These places we can visualize clearly thanks to the outstanding photographs from NASA. But my research is on subjects more remote than our little planetary system; locations too little understood for vivid pictures to form in my mind; places more mysterious than any corner of our planet. And of these the spot I would most like to visit is the centre of our Galaxy. Let me try to take you there.

Journey in thought

The journey to the heart of our Galaxy is enormously long. Measured at the speed of light 25,000 years would be required for the trip. In a Jumbo jet travelling since the Universe began, about 15 thousand million years ago, we would now have covered only half the journey. On this trip, therefore, we must journey faster than an airliner, faster even than light: as fast as thought itself.

We will course through the inner spiral arms of the Galaxy. Each is a huge tangle of stars and gas. Some of the stars have recently formed, while others are already ageing. The gas is densest near the younger stars, and there we can most readily study it. Mixed with the gas is a dribble of dust. What astronomers mean by dust is not

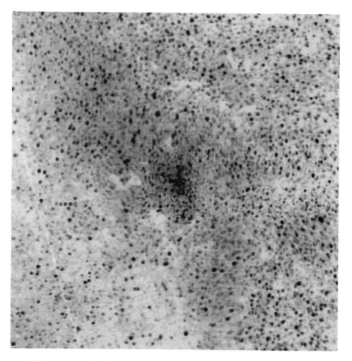

Figure 1. When the veils of dust are parted the central region of our Galaxy is revealed as an intense concentration of light. In this infrared image, as for all the illustrations in this article, a negative view is given to improve clarity, so stars appear black on a white sky. The small white blotches devoid of stars are opaque molecular clouds still lying in front of the star fields. The whole picture covers an area only one-sixth the apparent diameter of the Moon. (Anglo-Australian Telescope Board)

the fluffy stuff that annoyingly accumulates in the corners of a living room, but something more like ultra-fine sand. The individual grains are extremely minute, requiring a microscope to reveal any one, and again in contrast to household dust, in a roomful of the gas you would find only two or three of those motes. The gas itself is also extraordinarily tenuous – more so than all but the very best vacuums we create in our laboratories.

The amazing thing about this gas and dust, so rarefied that you could scarcely detect it with the most sensitive lab. equipment, is that you can't see through it. It's opaque. The reason is simple: the clouds are unimaginably big. A light beam setting out to traverse

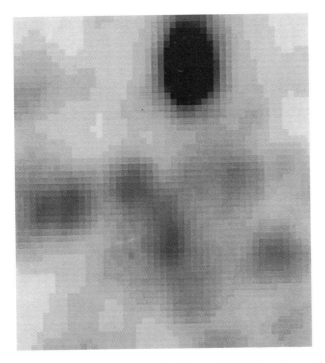

Figure 2. Detail in the central dark patch of Figure 1. This infrared image shows the innermost part of the Galaxy, and virtually all the stars seen are hot and young. The extremely bright source at the top is also a young, massive star, but is nearing the end of its life and has become a red supergiant. (Anglo-Australian Telescope Board)

one such cloud has to pass through so many living-roomfuls that it is virtually certain to bump into one of the motes of dust before journey's end. And when it does so the light is either deflected off course, or absorbed. So vast are these clouds that at the speed of light, a rate we have had to shun, the typical crossing time is several years; at the speed of a Jumbo jet a million years would be required. In our high-speed thought journey we can spare only a couple of minutes.

Try to imagine zooming through the starfields of our Galaxy. Stars large and small, yellow, blue, and white, fly past, like snowflakes on a winter's drive. At first the stars seem endless, though their numbers vary as you traverse local concentrations and sparser regions. But you gradually become aware that fresh stars are no longer appearing in front to replace those that have passed by. The numbers ahead dwindle steadily. Soon only a few lie in front. Perhaps nervously you glance back to ensure that not all the Galaxy's stars have been extinguished. They haven't. Ahead lie one or two stars with perceptible hazy patches beside them. They tell of a particularly dense gas cloud where the dust itself reflects back the light of stars close beside it. This is the clue to the empty sky beyond. Soon these stars too pass by; ahead is only darkness. We have entered one of the dense, dark clouds.

With eyes straining you become aware of a dim red star, redder than you thought stars could be. It brightens, and grows perceptibly orange, then yellow. Another faint red star appears, and a group of several. These are the stars that have newly formed behind the curtains of dust. Each is actually sun-white, but when first seen is veiled by so much dust that only the red light gets through. As you approach, less dust intervenes so that orange, yellow, and eventually all colours can reach your eye.

The passage through this hidden world ends, as subtly as it began. Gradually the number of dull red stars ahead increases as you approach the far side and leave behind the veils of dust. A new vista lies ahead, one never before seen. What will it contain? Perhaps our course passes a giant globular cluster, where several hundred thousand stars congregate together into a tight ball. Astronomers are still discovering globular clusters hidden behind dark clouds. Perhaps a glowing nebula, like the Great Nebula in Orion, becomes visible. Radio astronomers have mapped many such objects towards our galaxy's heart, none visible by optical techniques. Or maybe we will pass one of the more bizarre objects – a spinning neutron star, for example. But today there is no time to examine such objects. Our quest is to navigate the last opaque cloud that hides the very centre of our Galaxy.

Studying the heart of our Galaxy

We do not know whether on such a hypothetical journey the central regions would burst forth before us as we left behind the last dark cloud, or would instead very gradually be revealed as we traversed a long path of even more tenuous dust. We do not know, but we suspect the latter to be the more probable. We don't know because the study of the Galaxy's heart is a difficult business. The dust and gas prohibit observation at all optical wavelengths. X-ray observations have yet to provide major insights. Virtually all that we know of this region has been provided by infrared and by radio techniques. Both radio and infrared radiation penetrate the dust. Radio reveals the gas; infrared, being nearer to optical, shows the stars. One might therefore expect the two to paint the scene in complementary colours, but in fact the inferences each provides do not always agree, and the debates have been heated.

Inference here is the key word. With our senses dulled by the lack of optical information, all details of the central regions of our Galaxy have had to be worked out from the few clues available. And just as the reader half way through an Agatha Christie novel has probably reached the wrong conclusion, so may we. Interpretations and opinions change.

It is also important to recognize that we do not simply need to make a radio picture and an infrared picture, and set them side by side on our desks to map out the central regions. All observations, both radio and infrared, are technologically limited. As new equipment comes on line, new types of measurement can be made, some of which overthrow previous beliefs. It is, of course, the same in all areas of astronomy, but in this case the limitations of the technology are particularly influential. The description I shall give is the best available in early 1993. Some of the infrared observations that contribute to this description were made recently by myself and my colleagues, using the camera IRIS on the Anglo-Australian Telescope that was described in the 1993 *Yearbook*. Indeed, the observations are so fresh that this issue may be published before our technical papers.

The grand vista

However we came upon it, the Galaxy's centre would be an amazing spectacle. Look at any photograph of a spiral galaxy (like ours) and you will see that the concentration of stars is greatest in the middle. In our part of the Galaxy stars are several light-years apart. At the centre, they are separated by only a few light-days. That's one million times the concentration of stars we see around us. There would be no mistaking the centre, marked by a crescendo of light.

If we could journey into the midst of this region our sky would boast stars as bright as the full Moon, and so numerous as to dispel darkness permanently. Whereas our sky seems immutable, the stars of this hypothetical galactic centre sky would be ever on the move, the brightest covering several degrees per year relative to the fainter background specimens.

A few years ago the perceived wisdom was that these stars are without exception ancient. The brightest were thought to be red giants, like Aldebaran in the constellation Taurus, or Arcturus in Boötes. Such stars arise when sun-like stars become senile. The fainter stars are all smaller, yellow and orange dwarfs, well into middle or old age. We expect this population because the centres form first in galaxies, and rapidly convert the available gas into stars. There is then no fuel to make more. Young stars, bright, hot and blue, should be absent.

That this may not be the whole story has become apparent thanks to more careful studies of other spiral galaxies, for in increasing numbers we are finding rejuvenation to be the norm. More and more examples are coming to light in which new-born stars exist in significant numbers. The gas from which they form is also being found. And, of course, many spiral galaxies are now recognized to host the little-understood quasars at their hearts. Whatever quasars are, they most certainly are not old stars.

When we view any other galaxy, the innermost regions appear blurred together into a single point of light. The details cannot be made out, not even with the Hubble Space Telescope. The smallest feature we can make out comprises many millions of stars. The nucleus of our Galaxy is a great deal closer, and so provides the opportunity to disentangle the clutter. The more we study its innermost regions, within a light-year of the centre, the greater the range of phenomena we find. In particular, we have found many examples of young, hot stars. There is a cluster of maybe one hundred of them. They dominate the light output of the region.

Some of these are unusual stars, moreover, unlike any others known in our Galaxy, but similar to some of the brightest in our neighbour the Large Cloud of Magellan. They seem to be at a rare stage of their evolution, suggesting that all were formed in a single event several million years ago. Why this should be so remains one of the unanswered puzzles.

Gas in the centre

Some contribution towards an answer is provided by the radio observations. Surrounding the centre is a dense ring of cold gas. At least, it may take the form of a complete ring, or it may be a string of

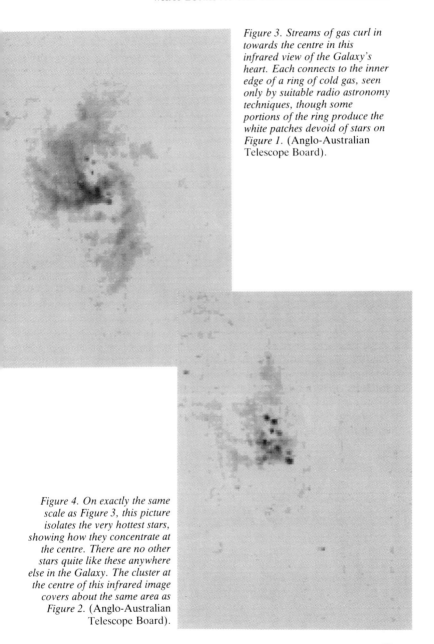

Figure 3. Streams of gas curl in towards the centre in this infrared view of the Galaxy's heart. Each connects to the inner edge of a ring of cold gas, seen only by suitable radio astronomy techniques, though some portions of the ring produce the white patches devoid of stars on Figure 1. (Anglo-Australian Telescope Board).

Figure 4. On exactly the same scale as Figure 3, this picture isolates the very hottest stars, showing how they concentrate at the centre. There are no other stars quite like these anywhere else in the Galaxy. The cluster at the centre of this infrared image covers about the same area as Figure 2. (Anglo-Australian Telescope Board).

clouds loosely connected together. If it is a true ring then we have difficulty explaining how it came into existence and how it survives. And whether it be a ring or a series of clouds, the fact that it does not lie flat in the plane of the Galaxy's spiral arms is an oddity.

The inner edge of this cold gas is illuminated by the young stars. Streams of heated gas pour off the ring and cascade into the centre in graceful curves. Although the gas flows at speeds measured in tens of kilometres every second, the distance is so great that we cannot see it change its position, and again must infer from limited data where it is travelling. The streams appear to converge close to the centre, where they probably collide and merge. Maybe it was a particularly violent collision that precipitated the formation of some massive stars a few million years ago.

The unusual nature of the hot stars has given rise to a number of alternative suggestions for their origin. In this crowded region, stars must sometimes make very close passes to one another. Such passes can cause gas to be transferred from one star to another, creating unusual configurations. Maybe these stars display their unusual properties because of a bizarre history.

Sgr A⋆

Radio maps show more than just the gas ring and streams. The brightest radio source in the region is an intense point known as Sgr A⋆. 'Sgr' is the standard abbreviation for the constellation Sagittarius, in which the galactic centre lies. In radio parlance Sgr A is the brightest radio source in that constellation, but it was named before detailed maps could be made. We now know that Sgr A is a complex series of radio sources which has had to be subdivided into Sgr A West, Sgr A East, and Sgr A⋆ (usually pronounced *saj-A-star*).

Sgr A⋆ is an unusual object. It varies slowly in intensity. It is known to be smaller than our Solar System. And to quite high precision it is not moving. This last point is a surprise given that the stars are all dashing round at high speed. To be so static Sgr A⋆ must either be very much more massive than stars, or to lie at the very centre of the Galaxy so that it feels equal gravitational pull in all directions. This second alternative is remarkably unlikely.

There is fairly widespread agreement that Sgr A⋆ is one of the recognized types of compact object, either a black hole or a neutron star. The former interpretation is preferred because no other known neutron star has the radio properties of Sgr A⋆. The essential question is its mass. Some astronomers have argued that

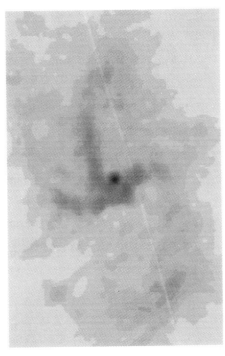

Figure 5. A radio view of the Galaxy's heart taken with the Very Large Array in New Mexico. This image shows the same hot gas as Figure 3, but in addition reveals the intense spot of radiation at the centre of the image. That is Sgr A*, a probable black hole, and has no counterpart in the infrared pictures.

the radio properties can be explained by a black hole of no more than 100 solar masses. Such an object could credibly have formed as a result of a massive star turning into a supernova. Infrared astronomers mostly argue for a much greater mass. They base their claim on the velocities of the gas streamers cascading in towards the centre. This hot gas can be seen by radio and infrared techniques alike. The velocity of the gas reflects the gravitational force it feels, which in turn gives clues to the distribution of material nearby. Several million times the mass of the Sun must be pulling the gas. Whether that mass can be accounted for solely by the concentration of stars, or whether an additional mass is required, remains a matter of debate. The most accurate measures seem to require Sgr A* to contribute about two million times the mass of the Sun, which would nicely explain why it is static with respect to the Galaxy.

If Sgr A* does weigh more than a million suns, it must be a black hole that formed at the same time as our Galaxy, and grew by swallowing gas and stars that ventured near. It must also now lie in a hole among the gas clouds, else it would be swallowing still and so be a much brighter radio source. It is surprising that, with so much gas flowing around, Sgr A⋆ could avoid scooping some up.

Another possible reason to doubt that Sgr A⋆ is so massive is the clusters of young, hot stars close to it. If the stars had been there for a million years or more, then the gravitational force of a million-solar-mass black hole should have been sufficient to disperse them to much greater distance.

These arguments and others can be heard bandied around in professional circles. The nature of the young stars and of Sgr A⋆ are by no means certain. Some of the uncertainties will be resolved when new technologies come on line, including the new generation of 8- and 10-m telescopes. Whatever we finally conclude lurks in this inner sanctum, there can be little doubt that it is a complex and vibrant place, crammed with unusual and fascinating phenomena.

How I wish I could visit.

Exploring Venus with Magellan

PETER CATTERMOLE

Problems of Venus exploration

From Earth we can never see the surface of Venus for the simple reason that it is permanently veiled by a dense layer of clouds which are composed largely of carbon dioxide (96 per cent) and nitrogen (3 per cent), and are opaque to radiation at visual wavelengths. Getting below this cloud deck and landing a probe safely is not a long-term solution to seeing what lies beneath, largely because the surface temperature is 850°F and the pressure 90 bars; this precludes the successful operation of optical and other instruments over long periods. To penetrate this veil it is necessary to use radar, a system which operates at wavelengths much longer than those which characterize the visual part of the electromagnetic spectrum.

During the 1960s, the giant radio telescopes at Arecibo in Puerto Rico and at Goldstone in California were aimed at Venus, and not only provided the first reliable data about its diameter (12,104 km) and rotation period (243 days), but also gave scientists the first glimpses of major surface features. Up to that time there had been much speculation about what lay beneath the optically impenetrable cloud mantle: did the planet have high mountains, water oceans, even volcanoes? The first radar images revealed that the planet had continent-sized highlands set amongst extensive plains. Subsequently the Russians actually landed probes on the surface, Venera 9 sending back the first panoramic, if somewhat myopic, view in 1975. This success spurred American scientists into building a more sophisticated radar system and putting it on board a space-craft which entered Venus's orbit in December, 1978; this was Pioneer Venus. It was with this craft that NASA scientists constructed the first topographic map of our sister world.

Despite this early success with radar missions, there was a need for higher resolution imagery and global coverage of the planet. Consequently, during the early 1970s, plans for a new and very sophisticated mission to Venus were drawn up by NASA. This was named Venus Orbiting Imaging Radar, or VOIR. However, the mission proved too costly to be viable and was scrapped during

1982. While the Americans were still deliberating, in late 1983 the Russian Venera 15/16 space-craft reached Venus and provided higher resolution imagery of parts of Venus's surface than had been previously obtained. This mission revealed un-Earthlike landforms on Venus called coronæ and arachnoids, and extensive global-scale ridge-belts.

Eventually, in 1983, a much-reduced mission objective saw the inception of VRM (Venus Radar Mapper). Its objectives were to undertake radar imaging, altimetry, radiometry, and gravity-field measurements. VRM was to have an elliptical polar orbit and, because there was a need to reduce the budgetary costs by one half, the VRM mission was to utilize proven technologies and spare parts from other programmes, such as Voyager, Ulysses, and Galileo. In 1986 VRM was officially renamed Magellan, and scheduled as the first space-craft to be launched by the Space Shuttle. A launch date was fixed but then hastily cancelled due to the Challenger disaster. The Space Shuttle Atlantis eventually took the 3,453-kilogram space-craft (costing US$551 million) into the sky on May 4 and, after a journey of fifteen months, entered a highly elliptical orbit around Venus. This crucial manœuvre happened on August 10, 1990. Magellan had successfully arrived at Venus. Almost immediately, a number of enigmatic problems arose and at one stage it seemed likely that the mission might be an expensive failure. However, these were rectified and mapping commenced in September 1990.

The Magellan space-craft

The Magellan space-craft is a low-cost, high-performance vehicle. Its main function was to transfer to Venus's orbit an array of radar antennæ, instruments, propulsion modules, solar panels and computers which would allow scientists on the Earth gradually to build up a detailed picture of the surface physiography and geology of Venus, backed up by gravity data. To achieve its objectives, Magellan carried four antennæ: a parabolic high-gain antenna (HGA) 3.7 m across, medium- and low-gain antennæ (MGA, LGA) and an altimeter antenna (ALTA). It also carried a radiometer.

As radar antennæ go, the 3.7-m dish of Magellan is rather small. The 'real aperture' of Magellan cannot provide high resolution imagery. As luck would have it, there is a trick which allows scientists to get round this problem: because a space-craft-mounted antenna is in motion while it is receiving echoes from a planet's surface, special computer processing can simulate a much larger antenna. Thus the distance the space-craft moves while a surface feature is within the radar system's field of view, effectively determines the functional size of the aperture. This is appropriately called Synthetic Aperture Radar, or SAR. The technique demands that the radar system can transmit and receive multiple outgoing pulses and returned echoes which, when studied on an oscilloscope, are seen to exhibit subtle differences in frequency which are caused by the relative motion of the target and the radar device. This is a manifestation of the well-known Doppler effect. Magellan's radar system is of this kind.

Also, because every radar pulse is electromagnetic radiation, its velocity of transmission is known; it travels at the speed of light in a vacuum. Since it is possible with modern technology to time, very accurately, the period which elapses between the transmission of a radar pulse and the time of return of the echo, radar may be used to undertake topographic mapping. Therefore, to complement the wide-angle, side-looking antennæ aboard the Magellan space-craft, there is a second, narrow-beam, horn-shaped antenna which points more or less vertically downwards. This is providing topographic transects of the Venusian surface and has allowed technicians to produce stunning 3D-simulations of some features.

On April 4, 1991, Magellan completed its primary mission: the mapping of 70 per cent of the surface of Venus (using left-looking radar); this had been achieved just one month short of the first 243-day mapping cycle (equivalent to one complete revolution of the planet beneath the Magellan space-craft). The second full mapping cycle was then completed (using right-looking radar) and 50 per cent of the surface imaged, including 14 per cent hitherto unmapped. On September 14, 1992, the third cycle, which commenced somewhat shakily on January 21, was also completed and will provide stereo coverage of roughly 35 per cent of Venus. There were future plans to lower the periapsis altitude of the probe from its present 290 km to 180 km, so that Doppler gravity field measurements could be made.

Mapping Venus with Magellan

Using its array of data-collecting instruments, Magellan completed a total of 1852 data-collection and playback passes of the planet during the first 243-day mapping cycle. Each of the mapping passes collected images over a swath of surface about 25 km wide and 16,000 km long. Magellan also imaged a new area of the planet at each pass, as the planet rotated slowly beneath the space-craft (which remained essentially fixed in inertial space). Magellan approaches as close as 294 km and recedes as far as 8743 km from Venus during each orbit. The imaging system is able to resolve objects as small as about 120 m – a major improvement on previous space-craft-mounted radar instruments and also the powerful Arecibo radar telescope. Each 3 hr 15 min orbital period is divided up into a number of shorter periods of (i) mapping, (ii) data playback, and (iii) idling time. This is because the complexities of a radar system mean that data cannot be collected and transmitted

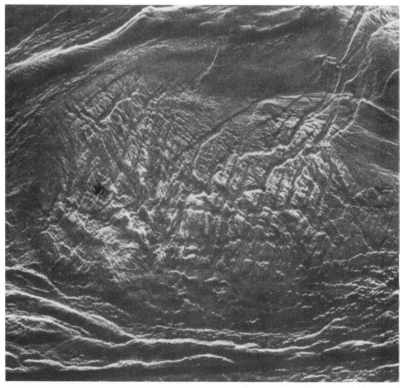

Figure 1. This image shows a 125 × 125 kilometres region on the eastern flanks of Freyja Montes in Ishtar Terra. (Courtesy NASA)

back to receiving stations on the Earth at one and the same time. The slow retrograde motion of Venus means that major topographic features, such as Beta Regio, Ishtar Terra and Aphrodite Terra, have been imaged in sequence as a function of days after Venus Orbit Insertion.

What is Venus like?

Magellan has shown that Venus can be thought of in terms of two principal landscape types: (i) volcanic plains, upon which are superimposed thousands of individual volcanic constructs and which cover 85 per cent of the globe, and (ii) tectonically-deformed highlands, which cover the remaining 15 per cent. Pre-Magellan data had already established that 60 per cent of the surface lies within 500 metres of the mean planetary radius of 6051.4 km, the predominant physiographic unit being rolling plains; in fact, an amazing 90 per cent of the surface lies within a 3-km height interval. The steeper slopes are located in the more elevated regions. There is also a broad tendency for the roughest surfaces – which show up bright in radar images – to coincide with the higher terrain, either delimiting highland massifs or the rims of raised circular features such as craters, or the tops of large domes.

As well as mapping highlands, lowlands and plains, fractures and faults, Magellan has revealed a number of features on Venus for the first time. These include wind streaks (familiar from the plains of Mars), extensive exposures of outflow materials associated with fluidized impact ejecta, lava flow lobes and different types of channels, æolian dunes, and impact craters as small as 1.8-km diameter. Adding these to the already fascinating tally of uniquely Venusian structures – coronæ, arachnoids and ridge-belts – it is clear that we are dealing here with a world in some ways Earth-like but in others, quite different. This has to reflect differences in the internal workings of the planet, particularly in the way heat is transferred towards the surface from the hot interior.

The highland region of Beta Regio, in particular, already had excited geologists after having been beautifully imaged from Arecibo. Magellan's enhanced resolution shows far more detail and shows not only the huge volcanic edifices of Rhea and Theia Montes, but also how in northern Beta Regio an area of very complex and non-volcanic terrain has been rifted apart. These complex regions were formerly known as tesseræ, and are uniquely Venusian. Arguably they are the most tectonically complex areas on the planet. Comprising a complicated network of intersecting troughs and ridges, they tend to occur as elevated plateaux with steep sides which are very rough at metre and smaller scales. First given the name 'parquet terrain', for obvious reasons, Magellan images essentially tripled the known extent of the tesseræ, which can now be identified in Tellus, Ovda, Thetis, Phoebe, Beta, and Asteria Regiones, and within the regions of Lada Terra and Nokomis Montes. The largest contiguous area of such terrain covers ten million square kilometres and stretches between Ovda Regio and the westward extension of Aphrodite Terra. Planetary scientists now tend to term these CRT (complex ridged terrain), to my mind a much less desirable term than 'tessera', if only for the difficulties of saying it!

As the first mapping cycle progressed, Magellan imaged the highland region of Lakshmi Planum, a massive volcanic plateau larger than Tibet, and the mountain massif of Maxwell Montes, well known as the highest point on Venus (over 11 km high). Lakshmi is nearly 5 km above the mean planetary radius and is surrounded by extensive belts of mountains with a ridge-and-trough morphology. Beyond the smooth upland plains are steep scarps which drop off as much as 2 km to surrounding tessera blocks. Magellan showed that the slopes of Venus's highest massif, Maxwell Montes, are amazingly steep: the west-facing slope has a gradient of over 30°!

To the south of the distinctive highland region of Ishtar Terra are the extensive lowlands of Sedna and Guinevere Planitiæ whose deepest levels descend 1 km below datum. These plains are punctuated by the isolated highland massifs of Eistla, Alpha and Bell Regiones. The former is dominated by the twin volcanic peaks of Sif and Gula Montes, 3.5 and 4.4 km high respectively, which are located astride south-east-striking rifts and associated with which are extensive volcanic flows. East from Guinevere Planitia, the surface rises along a belt of equatorial highlands which together comprise Aphrodite Terra, the most extensive highland region on the planet. This is roughly of the same area as Africa. There are several individual massifs, beginning in the west with the steep-sided scarps of Hestia Rupes, passing through Ovda Regio and Thetis Regio to Atla Regio, these being separated by deep rifts, such as Diana, Dali, and Artemis Chasmata. Atla Regio is particularly interesting, as it is the location of a group of massive volcanoes – Sapas, Maat, and Ozza Montes. Sapas Mons is a huge volcanic mountain with two peaks with summit depressions. Maat Mons is 400 km across and rises 8 km above Venus datum; it is the tallest volcanic construct on Venus.

Figure 2. Shows the volcano Sapas Mons (approximately 400 kilometres across and 1.5 kilometres high) in the broad equatorial rise called Atla Regio. (Courtesy NASA)

Each of the major highland areas is separated from the others by deep basins within which are located smaller uplands, such as Alpha, Bell, Eistla, and Tellus Regiones. Some of these are joined by deep rifts, while straighter but shallower rifts, arranged in parallel sets, cut obliquely across the equatorial zone. Magellan images have enhanced our knowledge of the fine structure of the plains above which the highlands rise. In particular, details of over 1600 volcanic landforms, of 175 coronæ, and of complex strain structures and deformational belts were revealed for the first time. The latter were first noted on Arecibo images, and tend to concentrate in or near broad topographic lows, particularly in Lavinia, Atalanta, and Vinmaria Planitiæ.

The plains play host to an enormous number of volcanic features. There are literally hundreds of volcanic centres, ranging in size from 500 km down to just a few km across. These include large volcanoes, steep-sided domes, calderas, and lava channels. Venusian 'shield fields' – clusters of small shield volcanoes 10–20 km across – are particularly interesting and imply rather different thermal conditions inside Venus than those known to prevail on the Earth.

The uniquely Venusian structures, coronæ, tend to avoid the true lowlands, but occur in large numbers in the rolling plains. This pattern may, however, be more apparent than real, since lowland coronæ may have been buried by lava flows that streamed down into the lowest ground from either side. Coronæ are uniquely Venusian, being huge circular to ovoid landforms showing raised rims and sunken moats. They are also crossed by fractures and partially buried by volcanic flows. Indeed in some cases the domical central regions of a corona may be studded with smaller shields or even shield fields. This association clearly implies they have an origin in volcanism and many scientists believe they grew (and perhaps are still growing) above upwellings in the Venusian mantle.

One landform type that I have not mentioned – surprising perhaps in view of their ubiquity on solid planetary bodies – are impact craters. Yes, these do exist. Indeed, by July 1992, Magellan had imaged 89 per cent of the globe and enabled scientists to catalogue 842 craters in the diameter range 1.5 to 280 km. Venus provides us with a unique opportunity to study the bombardment of a very different planetary surface than that of the airless Moon: one protected by an extremely dense atmosphere and, as it turns out, one where relatively little modification has affected the most recent cratering record. An extensive record of impact has been

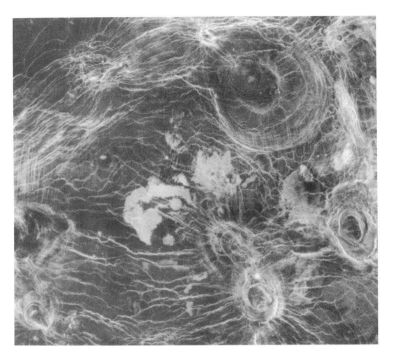

Figure 3. This mosaic shows features known as arachnoids that, so far, have been found only on Venus. They range in size from 50 to 230 kilometres in diameter. (Courtesy NASA)

preserved, but there is a lack of very small craters due to the shielding effects of the dense atmosphere.

Those craters larger than about 15 km in diameter are generally circular and similar to comparably sized craters on other planets; however, smaller ones tend to depart from circularity and have greater complexity. This is the reverse of the lunar situation and is a response to the greater density of the Venusian atmosphere. When all of the craters so far imaged are considered, there appears to be a progression of morphological characteristics which is size-related: thus the largest structures are multi-ringed, followed at smaller diameters successively by structures with double rings, craters with one ring, craters with a central peak, craters having structureless floors and, finally, irregular or multiple craters. The final group

143

represents a divergence from the pattern typical of the Moon, where the smaller craters are simple, bowl-shaped, and circular. It reflects the fact that smaller bolides simply break up during their descent through the dense Venusian atmosphere, forming crater groups on the surface. The smallest meteoroids do not get through at all: they burn up during their descent. This accounts for the absence of craters smaller than about 1.5-km diameter.

When the distribution and size of the craters preserved is considered in detail, and compared with that of the Moon, it suggests that large regions of the planet are no older than 500 million years, meaning that considerable resurfacing has affected the planet. Crater modification (and partial obliteration) is, by-and-large, concentrated in equatorial latitudes, where large patches of the plains appear to have been modified by volcanism.

Venusian impact craters have distinctive ejecta patterns and strange outflow features which suggest that entrained atmospheric volatiles caused fluidization of the ejecta, which flowed across the surface rather than being ballistically transported through the air. The roughness of the ejecta blankets around craters shows up as distinctive radar-bright lobes and sheets, and also dune-like patterns. Where the dust-laden atmosphere swept across the surrounding plains, scouring of the ground sometimes smoothed the surface, or deposited fine-grained particles producing radar-dark patches and wisps. Furthermore, much greater volumes of impact melt were generated during Venusian impacts than on either the Moon or Mars. Smooth, radar-dark, regions associated with the larger craters bear witness to this.

What have we learned?

Bearing in mind that Magellan mission scientists are involved in the detailed mapping of an Earth-sized planet, at a resolution equivalent to the best Earth-orbiting probes, it comes as no surprise to appreciate that there is an unprecedented amount of new imagery to be processed and inspected. Nevertheless, what the images show is a staggering improvement on anything we have hitherto seen and has meant the re-writing of many earlier ideas about the planet. Magellan has provided one of the most fundamental data sets ever obtained for a planet, and will occupy the attention of scientists for generations to come. One thing which is already clear is that volcanism has dominated the geological history of Venus, while tectonic activity has severely affected narrow zones, generating faults, and built amazingly complex blocks of intersecting ridges and grooves. The imagery which so far has been processed reveals a planet of immense complexity and with many geological features unlike anything known on Earth. A new geology is being written and will continue to be amended and extended as scientists gradually come to terms with it.

Infrared images probe deep into space

IAN S. McLEAN

Progress in studying the Universe has always been related to 'deeper' surveys of the cosmos, a quest for ever fainter objects, higher resolution yielding more and more fine detail and broader spectral response to sample **all** the energy forms passively collected by our terrestrial telescopes. Advances in technology in the past two decades have driven this quest at an astonishing pace. We now know of galaxies at 'redshifts' of four to five, potentially far enough away that we see them not as they are now, but as they were when the Universe was much younger. Studies of such incredibly faint objects are not easy! But study them we must if we are to understand anything about the formation of galaxies or the geometry and age of the Universe. Infrared Astronomy, itself undergoing a technology revolution, has contributed important new insight to these questions. Before we go any further however, it will be very helpful to review a few terms and concepts about cosmology.

We live in an expanding universe which appears to obey a simple law discovered by Edwin Hubble in the 1920s:

$$v = Hd$$

where v is the speed at which a galaxy at a distance d appears to *recede* from us. H is called Hubble's constant and, since d is a distance, H must have the dimensions of 1/time so that the product Hd is a speed. However, astronomers find it more convenient to express H as a 'speed divided by a distance'. If we measure speed in kilometres/second and distances in a special unit called Megaparsecs (1Mpc is approximately 3.26 million light-years or 3.09×10^{19} km) then the Hubble constant has a value of between 50 and 100 km/s per Mpc. Unfortunately, the exact value is debated hotly, and is still not known accurately because it is extremely difficult to derive the true distances to these galaxies unambiguously and independently. Note that $1/H$ is a time interval, it is known as the Hubble Time; if $H = 50$ km/s/Mpc then the Hubble time is about

20 billion years while if $H = 100$ km/s/Mpc then the Hubble time is only 10 billion years. The value of the Hubble Time is related to the 'age' of the Universe.

When astronomers speak about the 'geometry' of the Universe they are really talking about how the average distance between galaxies will change with time. There are essentially three cases, namely, *open*, *flat* and *closed*. In an open universe the expansion continues for ever, although the rate of separation will slow down. In the closed universe the expansion will eventually be halted by gravitational forces and will reverse direction into a contraction. The flat universe corresponds to the case in which there is a perfect balance so that the expansion will eventually stop but will not reverse itself. To distinguish between these possibilities we need to measure the amount of matter in the Universe to see if it is enough to cause the gravitational 'drag-force' needed to halt the expansion. Alternatively, we need to measure the rate of 'deceleration' of the expansion to deduce whether or not it is slowing down to a stop. There is a critical density of matter ϱ (the Greek letter *rho*), which gives precisely the flat universe and separates the open and closed cases. This density turns out to have the value $\varrho_c = 3H^2/8\pi G$, where H is the Hubble constant again, and G is Newton's Gravitational constant; since H is not known accurately the actual value of the critical density is somewhat uncertain but it is approximately equivalent to just one hydrogen atom per cubic metre! Astronomers express the observed density of matter in the Universe (ϱ) as a fraction of the critical density, i.e. $\Omega = \varrho/\varrho_c$ so that if omega (Ω) = 1 then the Universe is flat. The rate of deceleration of the expansion of the Universe is characterized by a number called q_0 (pronounced Q-nought) which is related to the density of matter (ϱ) by the simple equation

$$q_0 = 4\pi G\varrho/3H^2, \text{ which is just } \Omega/2.$$

Now, the expansion of the Universe with time means that the wavelengths of light (or radio) waves emitted when a source was young get 'stretched' by the amount of this expansion as the wave travels through space to distant regions. If the wavelength is stretched the light becomes redder. This is known as the cosmic 'redshift' and is measurable when the light from the distant source can be captured and spread into a spectrum since the atomic emission lines will be displaced from their normal positions. The displacement in wavelength divided by the original wavelength is called the redshift and given the symbol z. Note that the effect is similar to the familiar Doppler effect, but the redshift is not caused by relative motion in the normal sense but by the expansion of space itself. It is quite common to describe stages in the evolving Universe by their redshift z even when z is exceedingly large. An object with a redshift of 4, for instance, is being seen when the Universe was $(1 + z)$ times smaller, i.e. 5 times smaller than it is now.

The largest redshift object we know of today is the quasar PC1158 + 4635 at $z = 4.73$. It seems probable that this quasar resides in an underlying galaxy, because we know that to be the case for lower redshift quasars. Moreover, since the high redshift quasars are intrinsically extremely luminous – otherwise they could not be detected at such distances – it follows that the underlying galaxy is probably huge also, perhaps even more massive than our own Galaxy at 100 billion solar masses. If the quasar in these large galaxies is associated with a central black hole of large mass, then a substantial time is required for its formation and consequently, the underlying galaxy must be quite old already.

This was a quasar, what about a true galaxy? The highest redshift galaxy detected directly is the massive galaxy hosting the radio source 4C41.17 at $z = 3.8$ discovered by Chambers, Miley and van Breugel. Actually, we now know of about a dozen galaxies at redshifts $z > 2$.

The radio galaxies and quasars are evidence that large, massive galaxies existed at $z = 4$ to 5, that is, when the Universe was no more than one-fifth its present age. Unfortunately, this result does not tell us anything about how many less spectacular galaxies were in existence at that time. Since quasars and highly luminous radio galaxies are extremely rare objects it is possible that only a tiny fraction of galaxies formed that long ago.

How can we learn more about this early phase of the Universe? The first step is to take extremely long exposure images of regions of the sky well away from the plane of the Milky Way. Such regions at high galactic latitudes contain a minimum of foreground stars from our own Galaxy and allow us a clear, uncontaminated view of deep, intergalactic space. To obtain these deep images we cannot use photography, we need a detector of much, much higher efficiency. The answer is the Charge Coupled Device or CCD. The CCD was invented in 1970 at Bell Laboratories by Willard Boyle and George Smith and almost immediately found applications in astronomy. It is a small silicon chip containing huge numbers of individual, light-sensitive cells called *pixels* (short for picture elements), each one capable of converting photons of light into an almost perfect electronic image which can be digitized and stored in a computer. Today, CCDs are in widespread use, for example, almost every hand-held TV camcorder contains a silicon CCD chip. [For more about the CCD in astronomy see *Electronic and Computer-aided Astronomy; from eyes to electronic sensors* by I. S. McLean, Ellis Horwood Ltd., Chichester, 1989.] When a CCD camera is used on a large telescope and when many hours of exposures are combined it is possible to measure objects as faint as magnitude 27 in blue light (B = 27) and to just barely detect 29th magnitude objects in red light. One can then 'count' the numbers of faint galaxies per square degree on the sky in each magnitude interval. Optical number counts of faint galaxies have progressed extremely well using CCD cameras and are now being complemented by complete spectroscopic samples to about B = 24 to derive redshifts. A plot of the blue or B-band number counts is shown in Figure 1 on page 150.

What does the plot in Figure 1 tell us? Making the assumption that fainter magnitudes means more distant objects, then we would expect the number of galaxies per square degree on the sky, with roughly the same magnitudes, to increase as we progress to fainter and fainter magnitudes simply because our field of view encompasses an ever-increasing volume of space. However, the rise shown in Figure 1 is just too steep! We are forced to realize that galaxies in the distant past may not be quite like galaxies in the present. That is, there must have been some 'evolution' or change. For example, younger (high redshift) galaxies could be more luminous and 'bluer' because they formed many massive stars much hotter than the Sun and can therefore be seen to greater distances. Unfortunately, even when we try to include this effect we find that the blue number counts *still* rise more rapidly than any predictions, even including some extreme effects of cosmic geometry: an 'open' universe has more volume at high redshift than a 'closed' universe, and there is still more volume in a flat universe with a low density and an Einstein cosmological constant (an arbitrary force introduced by Einstein in 1917 to ensure that his field equations allowed for a static, non-expanding universe; Hubble's discovery of expansion was not made until 1929). Yet even these suggested models fail to explain the count discrepancy. Something is clearly wrong!

The first clue has come with the advent of deep spectroscopic data obtained with faint-object CCD spectrographs, often using 'multi-object' techniques such as optical fibres or multiple slits to get the spectra of many different faint galaxies at the same time. If you take a faint object and disperse its light into a spectrum, then each part of the spectrum provides even fewer photons to the detector, and therefore a much longer exposure is needed to get an accurate result. Even with the advent of optical fibres this kind

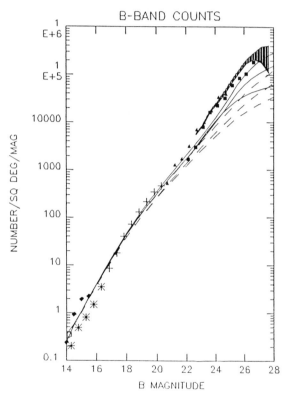

Figure 1. The number of galaxies per square degree per magnitude interval detected in blue light by CCD cameras is shown plotted against apparent blue magnitude. This graph is a compilation from the work of several groups including Metcalfe and others, Tyson and others, and Lilly and others. Two classes of model are shown. Dashed lines are models with no evolution or change in the luminosity of the galaxies with time, but include three different cosmological geometries ($q_0 = 0.5$ is the lower model in each case). Solid lines indicate the same three geometries but also include a prescribed way for the galaxies to change with time (or redshift). The blue number counts are higher than the most extreme models.

of observational work is very slow going and requires immense dedication. Pioneering work in this field has been done by Richard Ellis and his colleagues at Durham University. Figure 2 is a plot of redshift against B magnitude. Astonishingly, to B = 24 there is only one possible object which could even conceivably be at a redshift $z > 1$, the vast majority are at a redshift of less than 0.6. So, the faint objects distorting the blue number counts are *not* luminous galaxies at the edge of the observable Universe after all!

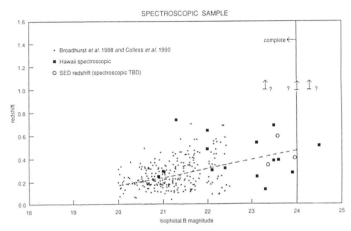

Figure 2. A plot of redshift versus blue magnitude for those galaxies whose redshift has been measured with a spectrograph. This is a compilation of work by Broadhurst and others, Colless and others shown by dots, and Lilly and others shown by solid squares. Nearly all objects are at z < 0.6.

What are these faint blue objects? One possibility is that there is a major population of dwarf galaxies (about 1 per cent the mass of our own Galaxy) that was present in the past at redshifts of about 0.3–0.4 but, for some reason, this class of galaxies is not present now. These dwarf galaxies are blue because they are forming stars and although very few of these stars will be massive blue giants like the stars of the Trapezium cluster in Orion, such stars are so incredibly luminous (over 100,000 × the Sun) that their bluish light dominates the light from the Galaxy. Another possibility is that the Universe has much more volume at low redshift than predicted by our favourite models. For example, in a flat universe of low density with a cosmological constant we could, with some galaxy evolution, probably explain the blue number counts without violating the spectroscopy constraints and also ease the problems of explaining the large-scale structure of the Universe, that is, how is it that the observed Universe is 'lumpy' with galaxies when the microwave cosmic background emission from the big bang is so extremely smooth?

But this is all conjecture. We need an observational tool which is more sensitive to cosmological geometry than the blue number counts. It would be better to look at galaxies in the infrared part of the spectrum instead of the blue because then we are detecting reddish light emitted largely from *old*, long-lived stellar populations (stars like our Sun, and all those less massive stars) whose ages are comparable to those of the galaxies themselves, whereas in the blue we are confused by the rapidly evolving hot, blue stars, which although very luminous, constitute only a tiny fraction of the mass of the galaxy. We need some sort of '*infrared CCD*' system. Easier said than done!

Three years ago, while still at the UK Infrared Telescope in Hawaii operated by the Royal Observatory, Edinburgh, I wrote an article for the *1989 Yearbook* describing a great technological breakthrough for infrared astronomy in which I was privileged to be at the forefront, namely, the advent of *infrared arrays* and I described the pioneering work which led to our new instrument called IRCAM (see *Astronomy Now* July 1989). Infrared arrays are small imaging devices similar to CCDs but operating in a slightly different way and, most importantly, manufactured from semiconducting materials other than silicon to enable them to detect infrared light and convert it to a measurable electrical signal. If the materials used are *indium antimonide* or *mercury-cadmium-telluride* the infrared camera will be extremely sensitive in the wavelength interval known as the 'near' infrared (from wavelengths of 1.0–5.0 microns). This is ideal for many reasons and is particularly powerful for cosmological studies, because at a redshift of $z = 3$ the spectrum of a solar-type star would be shifted from the yellow part of the spectrum to infrared wavelengths around 2.0 microns, a region known as the K band; note that CCDs are completely insensitive to wavelengths longer than 1.1 microns.

Using the IRCAM on the 3.8-m UK Infrared Telescope, Len Cowie, Simon Lilly, John Gardner, and the author began an ambitious programme in 1987 of very deep imaging in the K band in an attempt to compete with the optical surveys by CCDs. Since the night sky is extremely bright at infrared wavelengths – because everything is warm, even the telescope and the sky, and the upper atmosphere also emits an 'airglow' – it was by no means certain that we would be able to detect faint objects against this intense glare; it is worse than trying to locate a firefly walking across the lens of a distant and incredibly bright searchlight! It was a daunting challenge.

We developed a technique of taking numerous shorter exposures (typically 90 seconds each) of the region of interest, each time displacing the telescope by a few arcseconds in a repeatable, nine-point pattern before taking the next exposure; the pattern was repeated over and over throughout the night and on subsequent nights until fifty hours of observations had been accumulated! Since our fields were at high galactic latitudes and very sparse, we could programme a computer to analyse the stack of nine images on the assumption that the most frequently occurring signal at any location on the image *must* be the value of the sky brightness, therefore, any faint starlike object which caused a different value was immediately detected and removed in this first pass. These cleaned-up frames were then added to produce a 'master' frame which was an image of the sky itself with all sources removed. Next we asked the computer to divide each original exposure by this master frame, thereby eliminating to a very large extent the differences in sensitivity from pixel to pixel. At this point we could see that each of the corrected images now contained a few sources, some of which were clearly galaxies. Then we had to realign all the frames to a common centre from their offset positions in the nine-point pattern so that we could 'add up' all the exposures. As each hour, and then each night passed, more and more data were added and the final image became increasingly crowded as fainter and fainter objects began to appear. By this method, and after many long nights of work spanning several observing seasons, we were able to detect objects 100,000 times fainter than the night sky. From these observations we obtained number counts to a magnitude of $K = 23$ which is indeed comparable to the $B = 27$ limit of CCDs when one accounts for the relative brightness of galaxies at these two wavelengths; we had succeeded! The combination of the new technology and Len Cowie's drive and determination had won through. A typical small region of sky (5600 square arcseconds) as seen in the infrared is shown in Figure 3 as an image and in Figure 4 as a contour plot where it is compared to the optical view. About 300,000 objects per square degree are seen in the optical image and about 200,000 per square degree in the infrared image (Ultradeep K Band).

Figure 3. A very deep image in infrared light *of a small region of the sky. We can see that there are many galaxies per square degree in this deep image.* (Photo courtesy of Len Cowie)

Figure 5 shows the final outcome of all of this. Around a magnitude of K = 19 the number counts stop rising rapidly and change to a more gentle slope. What this implies is that the fainter magnitudes no longer sample to larger distances; we may have reached, at last, the magnitude at which we have 'broken through' to the end of the volume occupied by galaxies – a remarkable result! If so, the flat or slowly rising galaxy number counts in the infrared must represent the average shape of the galaxy brightness-versus-magnitude curve at the faint end. Comparing the K number counts with predictions we find that the best explanation is that we live in a universe with deceleration parameter of $q_0 = 0.5$, or a density parameter of $\Omega = 1$. Note that we are trying to explain a deficit in the number counts in the K band and so we cannot appeal to things like luminosity evolution, or claim that present-day galaxies merged from numerous fragments since these would go the opposite way. Moreover, *the stars giving the K band light were there for the whole cosmological lifetime of the galaxy* so there is no way to 'dim' the galaxy relative to its current luminosity.

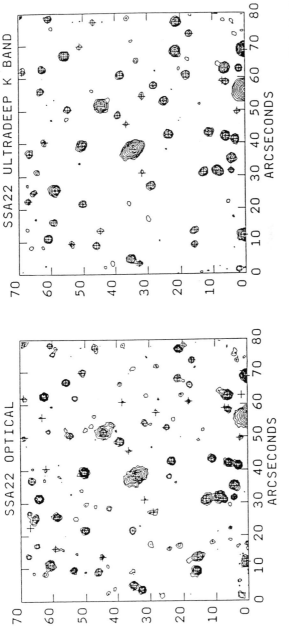

Figure 4. Very deep images of the small area of the sky in optical light (the sum of the B, V, and I bands) and again in infrared light (the K band at 2.2 microns). The objects considered to be well enough detected are shown by crosses and their contours of brightness. The correspondence is excellent.

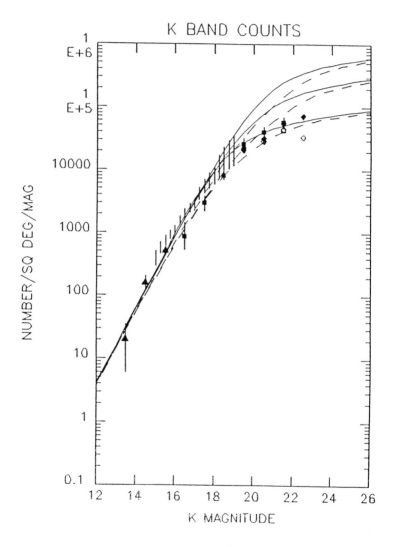

Figure 5. *The number of galaxies per square degree per magnitude interval detected in the infrared K band is plotted against apparent K magnitude just as for the blue number counts. The same models as before are plotted with dashed and solid lines. The K band counts fit best to a* $q_0 = 0.5$ *cosmological geometry irrespective of the degree of evolution (i.e. the lower dashed curve almost coincides with the lower solid curve).*

Of course, if the geometry of the Universe really does correspond to a 'flat' model then we certainly do have the problem of explaining the enormous excess of faint blue galaxies that lie at $z = 0.3$ to 0.4, and yet we don't see any similar population locally. Where have they gone? It is conceivable that these galaxies were disrupted in the star formation process or that they have faded to such a low surface brightness (magnitudes per square arcsecond) that we cannot detect them. Len Cowie has termed these objects as 'dead' galaxies.

If we interpret the K-band number counts at face value then the conclusion that $q_0 = 0.5$ ($\Omega = 1$) and that the cosmological constant is zero would be strong support for the inflationary Big Bang model. (This conclusion is also consistent with the announcement that instruments on the Cosmic Background Explorer (COBE) satellite have detected tiny fluctuations in the cosmic microwave background.) Most of the snags that arise in interpreting radio source counts and blue number counts are due to the transient nature of the events which provide us with an observable source, e.g. unusual activity in the nucleus of the galaxy and massive star formation respectively, and these events are short-lived (10–1000 million years) compared to the cosmological timescale. The K-band counts on the other hand correspond to stellar populations with lifetimes comparable to the cosmological timescale which makes them more immune to evolutionary corrections. Nevertheless, as Len Cowie, the pioneer in this field, points out, deeper K-band surveys are needed to confirm the trend in K-band number counts and it is especially important to obtain a complete spectroscopic redshift survey of faint K selected galaxies to be absolutely sure.

If a population of 'dead' galaxies exists then, as a result of the vigorous star formation at early times, it must have produced (by nucleo-synthesis in stars) a large fraction of the heavier elements now known, e.g. the carbon in our living cells and the iron in our blood. This population must have contained at least as much mass as the present-day 'normal' galaxies. Moreover, this matter could have been much more uniformly distributed than present luminous matter. This may be attractive to the Cold Dark Matter (CDM) theory, but there is also a piece of evidence against CDM theory, namely the existence of massive galaxies at $z = 4$ to 5. If it is shown that any part of these objects is dominated by an old population, older than 1000 million years, then we may run into serious time-scale problems because the Universe was not old enough at $z = 5$ in a closed cosmology.

This is certainly an exciting era for all astronomy, but it is particularly challenging for infrared astronomy. To improve the observational data base we need to develop larger and even more efficient infrared cameras and place these on the largest possible telescopes. Obtaining redshifts through spectroscopy will be a very important task for the new generation of large telescopes. In my new role as director of the Infrared Imaging Detector Lab at UCLA, I have now developed a new infrared camera with not one, but *two* arrays inside, each with a 16x as many pixels as IRCAM. We call the new instrument 'Gemini'. I am looking forward to using this instrument on the giant, 10-m W. M. Keck telescopes in Hawaii to continue to probe the depths of the Universe.

Acknowledgements

I am extremely grateful to my fellow Scot, Dr Len Cowie of the University of Hawaii, who has been inspirational with his dedication and leadership in tackling these problems, and in putting infrared arrays to such good use; it makes worth while the years of effort invested to develop the IRCAM instrument.

The Victorian Amateur Astronomer:

WILLIAM LASSELL, JOHN LEECH, AND THEIR WORLDS

ALLAN CHAPMAN

In the late nineteenth century, astronomy developed more rapidly, along more lines of investigation, than ever before. The distances of the stars were first measured, a new planet and many new satellites discovered, while spectroscopy, photography, bigger mirrors and lenses made possible the examination of many nebulæ and the chemical analysis of starlight.

Yet unlike today, frontier-advancing astronomical research was not considered as a professional activity, and those men who were the *real* professionals of the age, the Astronomer Royal and the University Observatory Directors, were *not* expected to do it. Their job, by contrast, was to monitor, refine and publish the constants of the known Universe, and, if one was in a university observatory, pursue such investigations as might amplify Newtonian dynamics. But if you wanted to determine the composition of Saturn's rings, search for change on the surface of the Moon, or try to resolve nebulæ, you had to pay for it entirely out of your own pocket. In other words, you had to be an amateur astronomer.

Victorian astronomy, as I shall be discussing in this article, covered a wide range of people, incomes, and levels of commitment, but where it differed most conspicuously from what we have today was in the presence of private individuals investing very large sums of their own money into private research. It would be hard to think of instruments like the Isaac Newton reflector or the Jodrell Bank Radio Telescope being devised, built, paid for and owned by a single private individual to whom astronomy was a hobby. Hardware of this calibre is now the product of elaborate team work, financed and owned by governments or wealthy academic corporations.

Yet the great telescopes of Lord Rosse and William Lassell were exactly in this league, given the differences in money values. Even when one considers 'lesser' figures, such as Lassell's friends James Nasmyth and William Rutter Dawes, or Sir James South, or William Huggins, the money which they freely expended out of their own pockets would be equivalent to sums argued over at length by the Science Research Council today. To such men, who were often willing to rifle their own and their families' fortunes for the advancement of learning, we must remain eternally grateful, for they were doing what was officially reckoned as 'private' research, in the days before governments recognized its international importance.

These were the 'grand amateurs' of Victorian astronomy, in so far as they did not hold professional jobs, although they were by no means scientifically uneducated. Lord Rosse, for instance, had obtained a first-class honours degree in mathematics at Oxford when he was twenty-one, Huggins had been educated privately before his father settled an income upon him, while both South and Dawes were medical men who had married very rich ladies.

Indeed, it is not easy, on this level, to decide where to draw the line between professionals and amateurs, after one has excluded such obviously paid professionals as the Astronomer Royal. We popularly think of Sir John Herschel as a 'professional' and Lord Rosse as an 'amateur', yet neither men had paid astronomical jobs, both were educated to a professional level, independently well off, Fellows of the Royal Society, and likely to attend the same scientific gatherings.

There were, however, men whom we might reckon more clearly as 'amateurs' because they came into astronomy in early retirement after achieving success in other careers. Admiral W. H. Smyth, the celebrated double-star observer and author of *Cycle of celestial objects* (1844), would be a case in point, along with Stephen Groombridge, a retired merchant, whose 1817 catalogue was better than anything produced to date by Greenwich. Francis Baily was an astronomical stockbroker, and a giant of the early Royal Astronomical Society. Yet the quality of the work which they produced was professional in every respect, as were the instruments at their disposal. Indeed, a commission to build an instrument of novel design had more chance of coming from a private individual (or amateur) in 1835 than it had of coming from a professional source.

Virtually all of the men discussed so far, with the possible exception of Lord Rosse, were engaged in a new and fast-advancing branch of astronomy: the measurement of double stars. Such stars were of especial interest because they promised, if measured carefully enough, to reveal two very important classes of information. Firstly, double stars were seen as the prime candidates for the revealing of parallaxes, from which stellar distances could be computed. Secondly, binary doubles and triples might be made to reveal the presence of 'dark companions', and demonstrate the action of Newtonian gravitation in deep space. For both classes of work, however, one needed excellent optics, with an established preference for big-aperture, highly corrected refractors, which even in those days could cost many hundreds, if not thousands, of pounds.

Double-star astrometry was a field already being pioneered by the Germans, who were also lucky in the respect that substantial state funds were being poured into such observatories as Dorpat, Berlin, and Leipzig. But for England to stay in the race, and add to the crop of discoveries, it was necessary for private 'amateurs' to come up with the money and do the work themselves. Smyth, South, and Dawes were England's double-star men. They all worked with refractors, and we must remember that the impetus which led Josef Fraunhofer, Peter Dollond, William Simms, and Alvin Clark to produce a succession of bigger and better object glasses before 1860 came from the demands of double-star astronomy.

But there was another type of 'grand amateur', interested in a different sort of research, who by the 1830s was turning to the neglected reflector as the ideal investigative tool. William Parsons, Third Earl of Rosse, was fascinated by the nebulæ described by William Herschel fifty years before, and their relation to the structure of deep space. Realizing the enormous 'space-penetrating' or resolving potential of big mirrors, with their single optical surface, over against the multiple surfaces of lenses, he created a scientific research establishment in the grounds of his Irish castle which was devoted to the perfection of *vast* mirrors. Complete with his own foundries, workshops, and carefully trained local men to do the work, Lord Rosse created the largest telescope of the nineteenth century in 1845. The six-foot mirror of 'The Leviathan of Parsonstown' gave us our first 'modern' glimpses of the spiral arms of the nebulæ and the structure of the Milky Way.

In spite of his academic scientific training and great personal wealth, however, Lord Rosse was an amateur, for by the obligation of his title, he was a professional statesman, with a seat in the House of Lords, and seriously taken responsibilities to the people of

Ireland. An indication of his amateur astronomical status can be seen in the fact that, between 1845 and 1848, his personal participation in research virtually ceased at Birr Castle, as he struggled to help alleviate the ravages of the Irish Potato Famine. By way of personal sacrifice, he devoted the revenues of his Irish estates to the assistance of the starving population.

Yet perhaps the most spectacular 'grand amateur' of the century was William Lassell of Liverpool. Unlike Rosse, with whom he came to correspond and visit, Lassell was born into relatively modest circumstances, in Bolton, Lancashire, in 1799. The son of a timber-merchant and builder, Lassell was given the 'commercial' education of a merchant, though from his teens, when he was apprenticed into the office of one of his Liverpool relatives, he set about reading everything scientific that he could find, as well as attending lectures at the Liverpool Literary and Philosophical Society.

Lassell's amateur status was everywhere evident until he was about forty, for though his notebooks, preserved in the Royal Astronomical Society, show that he was an expert mirror-figurer and observer by the time that he was thirty, he never relented from his first priority of establishing a highly successful brewery business. He was in partnership and trading under his own name by the age of twenty-five, and over the next forty-five years, his Milton Street Brewery was to finance one of the greatest astronomical enterprises of the century.

There were probably few times, moreover, when beer was in such apparently inexhaustible demand as in Liverpool during Lassell's years as a brewer. Liverpool was fast becoming one of the largest ports in the world, with vast armies of 'navvies' digging Jesse Hartley's beautifully engineered docks, not to mention railway workers, dockers, sailors, and travellers. And what they all had in common was thirst!

Throughout the booms and crashes of the mid-Victorian economy, Lassell's shrewd merchant's nose told him that if his money was in making beer, then he would never go broke. In the three brilliantly original telescopes which he personally designed and built between 1839 and 1860, one can trace parallels to major works of civil engineering currently going on in Liverpool. The beer that went down the throats of the navvies digging the Royal Albert and its adjacent docks in the 1840s and 1850s bore a direct relationship to the discovery of Neptune's satellite Triton and Saturn's

Hyperion, the first glimpses of Saturn's 'crape veil' ring, Ariel and Umbriel, which rotate around Uranus, the resolution of the head of Donati's comet and the identification of 600 new nebulæ. While it is true that Lassell's prototype 9-inch telescope – unique in being the world's first equatorially mounted, domed planetary reflector – was gradually perfected during the years of Lassell's rise to fortune, his 24-inch instrument of 1845 and 48-inch of 1859 seem to have been the fruits of bumper brewery profits. The dock contractors who employed the navvies often made their own contracts with brewers to supply their sites, where the workers were obliged to buy their gallon of beer per day from a monopoly supplier. Though I have found no such site contracts among the small number of Lassell's commercial papers that survive, they seem to have been a common practice in the Liverpool trade and were a sure way of making lots of money.

William Lassell was experimenting with speculum mirror alloys and making observations as early as 1822, and by 1828 possessed several like-minded astronomical friends in Liverpool. There were the King brothers, Joseph and Alfred, the sons of a mathematics and navigation teacher, whose sister Maria became Lassell's wife. There were also his friends Bywater and Nixon and the young William Rutter Dawes who combined the professions of physician and Nonconformist minister in nearby Ormskirk. Between them, these young men owned plenty of books, a good Dollond refractor and several reflecting telescopes. Like modern amateurs, they enjoyed testing each other's telescopes on difficult double stars, and on September 15, 1828 a group of them stayed up until four o'clock in the morning to take advantage of a clear sky. Dawes and the King brothers in particular became life-long friends of Lassell, and many decades afterwards, when Lassell moved his 48-inch telescope to Malta and Dawes had bought a Kent estate not far from that of Sir John Herschel, they remained in close touch.

Up to the age of forty, in 1839, Lassell showed all the marks of a committed amateur, who put his business first, and astronomy second. But by the time he had reached the mid-point of his 81-year lifespan, he was sufficiently established commercially to be able to devote more and more of his time and money to astronomy. After being elected F.R.A.S. in 1839 and F.R.S. in 1849, Royal Society Gold Medallist in 1849, Royal Medallist in 1858, and honorary Doctor of Cambridge University, he had become a world-class astronomer. Lassell was also an astronomical phenomenon in his own right, for not only did the money keep rolling into the brewery, to make his work entirely self-financing, but he showed *genius* as a telescope designer and builder, as well as user.

Though he had received no formal training as an engineer or optician, Lassell approached the problems of compensating supports, equatorial mounts capable of balancing a forty-foot *skeleton* tube, and the production of flawless 48-inch optical surfaces with an assurance which is breathtaking. Realizing around 1840 that it was impossible to make bigger mirrors of the perfection of his 9-inch by hand, he set about designing a machine. He crossed the Irish Sea to examine the machine with which Lord Rosse had ground his 36-inch mirror, built a duplicate in his Liverpool workshop, and quickly diagnosed its faults.

It was at this stage that Lassell met a like-minded man who not only assisted him to design and build the prototype of all subsequent large, optical grinding machines, but also became another lifelong friend. This was James Nasmyth, a man nine years younger than Lassell, who by his late forties would retire from the running of his Manchester engineering factory to devote his time to lunar and solar astronomy. Independently famous as the inventor of the 'Nasmyth steam hammer', and an early mass-producer of railway engines, he was the man whose workshops could make hundreds of tons of metal work to a hairsbreadth. Nasmyth was already a skilled hand-figurer of specula, and when Lassell saw one of 10 inches, he claimed that it 'made my mouth water'.

Although Nasmyth's engineering factory built the two large figuring machines that used steam power and elaborate gear races to produce the curves of the 24- and 48-inch mirrors, Lassell made it quite clear that they, and the telescopes that they made possible, were entirely of his own devising. Nasmyth was Lassell's friend, advisor, and heavy contractor, but the vision and designs were Lassell's own. This is clear from the superlative engineering drawings and calculations, in Lassell's own hand, preserved in the R.A.S. Library, as well as in his R.A.S. paper of 1848 wherein he describes the 24-inch telescope.

In addition to the growing array of domes in the grounds of 'Starfield', his suburban Liverpool observatory-mansion, there were also sophisticated workshops, which he proudly showed to visiting astronomers from across the world. It was in these workshops that he melted down 295 pounds of pure copper, 136 pounds of best granulated tin, and 18 pounds of white arsenic to cast the

24-inch mirror, prior to grinding it on the steam-driven Lassell–Nasmyth machine.

By the late 1840s, Lassell was conducting an international correspondence, and finding that 'Starfield' was one of the places in England which visiting foreign scientists often wanted to see. In 1850, for instance, Professor Wilhelm Struve, Director of the Pulkowa Observatory in Russia, stayed at 'Starfield', followed a few days later by the Astronomer Royal, who called *en route* to Greenwich from Scotland. Lassell now moved with sufficient ease amongst these luminaries for Maria Lassell to press the Astronomer Royal into service to take one of Struve's forgotten shirts and return it to him in London. One had to know G. B. Airy *very* well to ask him to carry laundry around England!

Lassell became a corresponding friend of W. C. Bond, Director of the Harvard College Observatory, in America. It is probably true to say that, between them, Lassell and Bond were the world's leading experts on the outer planets in the 1840s. Working with the fine 15-inch Merz refractor at Harvard (which was eleven degrees of latitude closer to the equator than Liverpool), Bond had the advantage of having less atmosphere to look through, making the ecliptic eleven degrees higher, which was vital to seeing delicate planetary detail. Lassell and Bond made several simultaneous discoveries, such as the Crape Ring of Saturn (along with Dawes), and Hyperion, the seventh satellite of Saturn.

It was also a pity that when John Couch Adams computed a place for the suspected 'planet beyond Uranus' in 1845, he did not contact Lassell. When Neptune was eventually discovered at the Berlin Observatory on September 23, 1846, using Le Verrier's co-ordinates, Lassell decided to look for it from Figures published in *The Times*. Not only did his 24-inch reflector reveal an immediate *disk*, but by October 10, 1846, he had discovered its satellite Triton, and suspected the presence of an equatorial ring like that of Saturn. For six years, he reported the positions of this ring to the R.A.S., before writing it off to a flexure in the mirror in 1852. It is unlikely, alas, to have any connection with the flimsy Neptunian ring discovered by *Voyager II* in August 1989, though one cannot help wondering.

The growing industrial sprawl of south-east Lancashire was causing a rapid deterioration in seeing conditions, and on one occasion in 1847, Dawes humorously re-named his friend's observatory 'Cloudfield'. It was a pursuit for pure skies, thereafter, that caused

Lassell to take the 24-inch to Malta between 1852 and 1853. So pleased had he been with the results, that when he was completing the 48-inch in 1859, he realized that it was useless to set it up in England on a regular basis. It became, therefore, the first big telescope designed for, and used exclusively in, a foreign prime-sky location, as the entire Lassell household, complete with steam-powered polishing machine, 270 crates and grand piano, returned to Malta between 1861 and 1865. The rich crop of discoveries which Lassell made in Malta, and which at last enabled him to steal a friendly lead on W. C. Bond and his astronomical son, George, as the island was 6½° further south than Harvard, provided ample demonstration of the advantage of big telescopes in tropical locations. Whenever we think of contemporary discoveries made in the Canaries, Hawaii, or Australia, we must remember the English *amateur* who led the way. Translated into modern terms, it was the same as the La Palma Observatory being the brain-child and private property of a single individual!

But not all amateur astronomers of the Victorian age were 'grand' in the way that Lassell, Rosse, Nasmyth or even Dawes were. In addition to the rich, astronomy also appealed to those of more limited resources, and even to some who were on the poverty line.

John Tregent must have been one of Victorian astronomy's most enterprising characters, for though, as a tailor by trade, he was an amateur, he made a substantial supplementary living as a street telescope demonstrator. He was one of the persons interviewed in 1856 by that celebrated 'investigative journalist' Henry Mayhew, who wrote a detailed account of Mr Tregent's activities in his *London Labour and the London Poor* (1861–62).

Like so many amateurs, John Tregent was fascinated by scientific instruments early on in life, found out whatever he could about them, and started to experiment with lenses. He was particularly enthused when a stranger whom he met in a London park allowed him to have a look through his pocket telescope. Using his hard-earned savings to buy the cloth, Mr Tregent paid an Islington optician five suits of clothes to make a small refractor for him, although it turned out to be optically useless! On the other hand, it must have been an elegant piece of brasswork, for Tregent sold it for £20, and used the profits made on the deal to acquire a series of refractors which culminated in a 4½-inch instrument magnifying 300 times and costing £80. This would have been easily equivalent to several thousand pounds in modern money.

In addition to any private observing which John Tregent might have done, he found that the public was willing to pay good money – one old penny, or one 240th of a week's wages – for a look through the instrument, along with a short talk on the wonders of the heavens. Jupiter, Saturn, and the Moon were well-tried favourites on clear nights, though it does not seem to have been possible to see much in the way of stellar objects from the smoky, gas-lit streets of early Victorian London. The best patches were outside pubs, for when the word got around that a telescope show was outside, Mr Tregent found that hoards of enthusiastic boozers would pour out, sit in the gutter nursing their pots of beer, while they waited their turns for a glimpse at the sky.

Considering the endemic violence of early Victorian London, it seems remarkable that Mr Tregent never suffered any trouble with his valuable instruments. Perhaps his way with words, and obvious sense of racy humour (aided, no doubt, with a stout stick) stood him in good stead, although his activities were not without occasional mishaps. On one occasion, when a tipsy man was looking through the telescope, the tripod slipped, giving him a black eye with the eyepiece. The man howled with terror exclaiming that he had been hit by a falling star!

Amazing though it may seem, John Tregent claimed that he took £125 per year in pennies in the evening streets of London. That was equivalent to 30,000 peeps through his telescope. In 1856, when a working man would have been lucky to make 25 shillings (£1.25) for fifty-odd hours of hard work, John Tregent was making a lower-middle-class income from his hobby alone, not to mention what he made as a tailor by day. One wonders at the grounds upon which he qualified as one of London's 'poor'.

John Tregent was clearly an astute, self-educated amateur astro-nomical promoter, who was familiar with several aspects of con-temporary 'professional' astronomy, and displayed an expert knowledge of what to look for when buying an object glass. He considered that good object glasses started at around £30, and were only worth while if a star image remained a pinpoint even at the highest magnifications. The Reverend Mr Cragg's great telescope at Wandsworth, with its 24-inch object glass by Ross, had been a failure, said Tregent, in spite of the alleged £6,000 spent on the objective alone. As Mr Tregent so graphically put it:

'Men have been known to throw their heads under waggon wheels . . . from being regularly worn out with working an object glass and not being able to get the convex right.'

Astronomy was a subject of great popular interest in the nineteenth century, and formal lectures upon it could draw substantial audiences. Professor Nichol addressed a large audience in the Salford Mechanics' Institution in the early 1840s, and when George Airy, the Astronomer Royal, lectured on his recent gravitation researches conducted at Harton Colliery in October 1854, five hundred persons (including many working men with complimentary tickets) packed themselves into a room measuring 46 by 30 feet in the South Shields Central Hall, to hear him. In 1861, Airy addressed an incredible 3,000 people in Manchester's Free Trade Hall on the dynamics of the Solar System. And that was long before the invention of electrical amplification equipment.

But in addition to the big names, it seems that almost anyone could draw a paying crowd for a lecture on astronomy, especially if it was advertised as being accompanied with models and instruments. When Mr Children, an enterprising Bethnal Green bootmaker, hired a London lecture hall around 1840, he soon found that some of the audience knew more about astronomy than he did. The wonderfully ignorant Mr Children's repeated references to 'the *consternations*' of the sky soon produced roars of laughter and catcalls from his audience.

But quite undaunted, the budding astronomical educator quickly learned by his mistakes, and was soon able to relinquish his old trade, pocket the profits of the sky, and purchase a large farm in America.

Nor must it be forgotten that amateur astronomy forms the scenario of one of Thomas Hardy's most controversial early novels. *Two on a Tower* received gasps of disapproval when it first appeared in 1882, being concerned as it was with the very earthy desires of a beautiful widow of thirty for a handsome local lad of nineteen whose interests so far had been entirely celestial. Swithun St Cleve, the orphaned son of a poor clergyman, accidentally smashed the object glass which he prized so dearly, giving Lady Viviette the opportunity to replace it with a superb, equatorially mounted refractor which she proceeded to install on top of a tower on her estate.

What happened after that is best found out by reading the novel, although Hardy does include some of the most exquisite descriptions of the night sky to be found anywhere in English literature between the incidents which led to a child being born to her Ladyship and Mr St Cleve going to South Africa in the tracks of Sir John Herschel. To get the astronomical details as accurate as possible, however, Hardy claimed that he visited the Royal Observatory, to see what large refractors and their domes looked like.

Victorian amateur astronomy was practised by many types of people, rich, poor, and fictional, though one of its most earnest devotees must have been John Leech of Frodsham, Cheshire. In 1869, Mr Robinson, a kindly local gentleman of Frodsham, approached William Gladstone, the Prime Minister, in an attempt to obtain some sort of public support to aid John Leech in his astronomical studies. Leech was a working shoemaker who, according to the 1871 Census Return, had been born forty years previously, in Heywood, Lancashire, and now pursued his trade in Frodsham and with his dressmaker wife was struggling to bring up three small children.

Mr Robinson's letter was passed on to the Astronomer Royal, as the Officer of State best qualified to deal with it, and once the methodical George Airy had got the bit between his teeth, a remarkable correspondence came to pass between Greenwich, Westminster, and Frodsham. Judging from Leech's letters, still preserved in the Royal Observatory archives, he had only received a rudimentary formal education, for while his penmanship was excellent, his grammar and spelling were shaky, and his punctuation scarce. Even so, he had already passed beyond elementary astronomy and taught himself enough French to work his way through Pontécoulant's *Théorie analytique*.

It seems to have been John Leech's desire to give up shoemaking and devote himself to astronomy full time, but the Astronomer Royal was quick to point out that no appropriate jobs existed at Greenwich, or elsewhere, for which he would be suitable. On the other hand, an official invitation was made to Leech to specify how, within reason, the government could assist with his studies, especially as he seems to have been in the habit of passing his knowledge on to his fellow artisans.

Airy and Gladstone received the hard-up amateur astronomer's eternal request: a good telescope. Leech wanted an equatorially mounted achromatic refractor (like Hardy's Swithun St Cleve), though he was modest enough to say that he would be delighted instead to have a device called 'The star-finder' which he had seen advertised at £5. 15s. 0. (£5.75) in a paper. But amateur astronomy now threatened to become a politically sensitive subject, for if the word got out that the government was giving away refracting telescopes to enthusiastic amateurs, then how could Gladstone's controversial Income Tax be kept within bounds? Even a 'low-class', non-equatorial 4-inch refractor would have cost £28 in 1869 (much less than John Tregent's instruments), besides which the Astronomer Royal believed that John Leech could be better helped by being given some educative devices, rather than a relatively commonplace telescope.

I have calculated that Airy devoted at least thirteen hours of working time to John Leech, or about £16 of official salary time. This included serious thought as to how the Frodsham amateur could get the most useful devices for the minimum cost to the public purse, along with official recommendations as to how Messrs Horne and Thornthwaite might improve their little equatorial 'Star-finder' by equipping it with a 1¼- as opposed to the standard 1-inch aperture telescope. Eventually, the delighted shoemaker received a large box containing a 'Star-finder', globes and some minor pieces. In total, these items had cost Queen Victoria's government less than £12, which in itself would have been equal to eight or ten weeks' wages for John Leech. His rapturously grateful letter of thanks gives a fitting end to this saga of humble scientific aspiration, though one cannot help wondering how much energy, intelligence, and talent was being allowed to go to waste by keeping John Leech in his 'place'.

But if one chose to view the John Leech episode with a tinge of cynicism, one might say that Gladstone saw good election propaganda in it. In 1867, the working man received the vote for the first time, and Gladstone's Liberal Party possibly recognized that one way to get Liberal praises sung by the working men of Frodsham was to give some official encouragement to a future voter in the town.

Serious amateur astronomy has never been cheap, though the modern observer can at least console himself with the fact that today it is cheaper, in relation to average earnings, than it has ever been before. When John Herschel published his *Astronomy* in 1833, in a small format and cheap binding, it cost six shillings (30p) per copy. Five or six shillings remained a fairly stable small book price down to the Edwardian era, seventy years later, when Sir

Robert Ball's *Story of the Heavens* (1886) still cost 12 shillings and sixpence (62½p). For a working man, such as a carpenter or shoemaker, these sums would have represented between one-quarter and one-half of a whole week's earnings. It would have been like paying £40 or £50 for the present *Yearbook*.

Yet these relatively elementary books still demanded a high level of literacy, not to mention numeracy, to understand them, for unlike today, there was a distinct shortage of elementary books aimed at the beginner. So getting started was not easy, even if you had the money. Although it is true that Public Libraries began to appear in many towns after 1851, they were frequently off-putting and formidable to those who needed them most. Many Borough Librarians, moreover, saw it as their primary duty to stock standard reference books and not waste ratepayers' money on simple texts. Many ordinary people were further put off joining libraries because they had to be vouched for by a clergyman or magistrate, and shown to have clean hands.

As we saw with the attention lavished upon John Leech, even the most elementary telescopes were hopelessly beyond the pockets of all but the relatively well-off amateurs, for even a senior clerk in a solicitor's office would have to spend between two and three months' salary to buy a modest refractor with stand and fittings.

Victorian amateur astronomers lived, quite obviously, a universe apart from each other, when one compares William Lassell with his tens of thousands of disposable pounds, and John Leech with his £12 gift from Gladstone. The only alternative was to follow the route taken by the ingenious John Tregent, and buy bigger telescopes from the proceeds of an astronomical peep-show.

By contrast, how fortunate we are today, when for the modest sum of £130 one can buy a cheap Japanese refractor, a beginners' textbook, and still have enough left to join a local astronomical society.

The Victorians were a highly sociable people, and sought to bring like-minded (and by definition, like-pocketed) people together into organized societies. Modern town councils, trades unions, the London clubs, and the Football Association were all products of the Victorian organizing passion. As a dominant concern of the day, science soon became a subject of social organization, and from 1820, the R.A.S. became the natural focus for wealthy, leisured astronomers, although dogfights sometimes broke out between headstrong amateurs like the surgeon Sir James South and Cambridge mathematicians like Richard Sheepshanks.

In the same way that astronomical topics were favourites at meetings of the middle-class Literary and Philosophical Societies around England, so the working men went to hear them in their Mechanics' Institutions. After all, to men who were obliged to spend ten hours per day underground or working in grim factories, astronomy, with its connotations of limitless space and sparkling light, had an immediate appeal.

But it is fitting to think that the city in which one of Victorian Britain's leading amateurs worked for forty years was to be the home of the first *specialist* amateur astronomical society outside London. Though not directly connected with William Lassell and founded in the year of his death, 1881, the Liverpool Astronomical Society indicated the shape of things to come in numerous other towns around Britain.

In 1881, the Reverend T. E. Espin and a number of friends formed an amateur astronomical society in Liverpool which immediately exploded into one of national standing. By 1886, the L.A.S. had over 1,000 members across Britain, with requests for membership from persons around the world. Its published 'Proceedings' were acknowledged internationally, while its section heads conducted a correspondence with America and Australia. By 1890, it was felt by many, including Walter Maunder of the Royal Observatory, Greenwich, that a metropolitan-based amateur society was needed, which led to the founding of the British Astronomical Association in October 1890.

In its attempts to organize serious amateur astronomers across the country, the B.A.A. acknowledged the need for provincial branches, the first of which was founded in Manchester in 1892. But following the same paths of tension and competition along which many other Victorian metropolitan–provincial organizations had passed, the large and buoyant Manchester branch of the B.A.A. declared independence in 1903, to create the nation's second city astronomical society after Liverpool.

After the founding of the London-based B.A.A. in 1890, the Liverpool society (which had affiliation to its own offshoot) became a society serving the needs of a relatively local body of astronomers, though this was in itself quite large and active. The Society then received the gift of a fine 5-inch Cooke equatorial from Mr Rylands of Warrington, while in 1896, the Manchester Society obtained access to a 6-inch refractor in a nearby college.

Both of these societies enjoyed a distinguished roll of members. Such figures as Asaph Hall and Schiaparelli – not to mention the ill-fated Emperor of Brazil – were members of the L.A.S., while Manchester had Sir Howard Grubb, Sir Robert Ball, and Professor Gore.

Astronomy achieved something of a civic status in some British towns by the early twentieth century, as local observatories were made accessible to the public. Some of these institutions still survive, and continue in their role of making the skies accessible to the ordinary citizen, largely under the guidance of local amateurs. The 'civic' observatories in Preston, Lancashire, and Dundee are perhaps the longest standing in this respect, while the Manchester and Liverpool societies' observatories had long since begun the tradition of having open nights for the general public. Most of the societies formed since World War II which have observatories of their own continue and greatly extend this public educational amenity.

Several public schools began to cultivate astronomy in the late nineteenth and early twentieth centuries, with observatories and astronomical societies. The most famous and scientifically significant of them was the Jesuit College of Stonyhurst in Lancashire, where the eminent schoolmaster and astronomer, Father Stephen Perry and his colleagues, performed pioneer solar physical work. Father Perry died returning from an eclipse expedition to South America in 1889.

Amateur astronomy also provided a vocation for many women in the late nineteenth century, for the Liverpool and Manchester Societies and the B.A.A. always had active women members. Barred as they were from most professions and London learned societies, and having the most restricted access to higher education, many intelligent middle-class women found amateur astronomy to be an ideal outlet for their energies. Jane and Caroline Lassell had assisted their father in his Liverpool observatory, and were probably the first persons in England after William himself to see Neptune's satellite, Triton. Though not active observers in their own right, they seem to have been sufficiently acquainted with their father's scientific business to correspond about it with William Holden of the Lick Observatory in California after their father's death. They were also made honorary members of America's prestigious Astronomical Society of the Pacific.

Miss Elizabeth Brown of Cirencester was an eminent solar

observer, a Solar Section Director of the Liverpool Astronomical Society in the 1880s, and later of the B.A.A. Agnes M. Clerke of Ireland was one of the nine or so women honorary (i.e. non-Liverpool resident) members of the L.A.S. in the 1880s, and earned her living as an author. Indeed, Agnes Clerke was one of the most successful scientific writers of the day, and the popularity of her books can be gauged from their continuing appearance in second-hand shops a century after their publication. Agnes Giberne's *Sun, Moon and Stars* (1879) was another best-seller, along with Miss Giberne's *Radiant Suns* and *The Ocean of Air*, each of which sold for 5 shillings (25p) per copy in the 1880s. At least, Agnes Giberne styled her books as for 'beginners'.

Given access to *Encyclopædia Britannica* to get started, the means with which to purchase reference books, subscribe to R.A.S. journals (though not become Fellows), and buy a good telescope, many Victorian women became accomplished practical astronomers. It goes without saying, of course, that most of these ladies were single and comfortably off financially, though their contributions both as observers and astronomical communicators were very great.

From the late 1870s, one finds a tiny number of women being admitted to British universities, where science subjects proved disproportionately popular in relation to their numbers. Organizations like the Oxford and Cambridge University Extension and Summer Schools from around 1880, and the Workers' Educational Association soon afterwards, found themselves heavily subscribed with women students (as they still are), often desiring scientific courses.

One of the great lady 'amateurs' of this period was Miss Annie S. D. Russell, who in 1895 became the wife of Walter Maunder, co-founder of the B.A.A. But Annie Russell had been one of the first women to receive a professional scientific education in England, when, in 1889, she graduated as a 'Senior Optime' in mathematics from Girton College, Cambridge. She went on to be one of the first women employed on the staff of the Royal Observatory, although in a job that was traditionally reserved for young lads of eighteen fresh from grammar school: a mathematical 'Computership'. It was at Greenwich that she met her husband, Walter Maunder, who was head of the Observatory's Photographic Department, although his academic scientific qualifications were inferior to her own.

Annie was obliged to resign from her Observatory position

(it being a Civil Service appointment) when she intended to marry Maunder, after which she devoted the remaining fifty years of her life to high-level amateur astronomy. A major presence in the early B.A.A., she became (like the recently deceased Elizabeth Brown) an eminent solar observer, and travelled both with her husband and on her own to observe eclipses around the world.

After its founding in 1890, the B.A.A. set about providing leadership to British (and Empire) amateur astronomers and co-ordinating their results. Yet by modern standards, it must have seemed a thoroughly middle-class Victorian organization. Its first President, Captain Noble, was a wealthy retired military officer (proudly photographed with gun and boots at the door of his mansion), its one pound per year subscription, though much cheaper than the R.A.S., was equivalent to a whole week's wages for a labourer, while its Wednesday afternoon meeting-time pre-supposed a leisured membership with easy access to the West End of London. Today, however, while retaining its Wednesday after-noon meeting-time, the B.A.A. caters for a much wider range of people than could have been imagined in 1890, including a junior section. But it is appropriate that it chose to hold its 1990 Centenary Out-of-Town meeting in Liverpool in recognition of the Society from which it originated, and to which I had the honour of deliver-ing the William Lassell lecture.

In was in Victorian Britain that the amateur astronomer came into being as a scientific type. Emerging from the general body of wealthy scientific gentlemen of the Georgian age, whose landed investments removed any need to work, the true 'amateur' came to be identified as the man who had an occupation but who did astronomy in his spare time. Wealthy as many of these persons were from the proceeds of their professions, and often excellently edu-cated, they were free to inject enormous dynamism into their subject.

Men like Lord Rosse and James Nasmyth belonged, in the words of Sir John Herschel when he presented the R.A.S. Gold Medal to Lassell in 1849, 'to that class of observers who have created their own instrumental means, who have felt their own wants, and supplied them in their own way'.

But one of the beauties of amateur astronomy was that a person did not have to have the wealth of a merchant prince to enjoy and make serious contributions to it. Clergymen, like the Reverend T. E. R. Phillips, lawyers like W. H. S. Monck, and ladies like Miss

Brown or Annie Russell could all do valuable work. Yet what all of these people still had in common with Lord Rosse and Lassell was not only the secure fact that they were far from poor, but equally significant, that they were in command of their own time. A country clergyman with £500 per year and a free Rectory could not only afford to splash out £300 on a telescope, but could also stay up until three o'clock in the morning looking through it if he chose. But no such freedom would have been available to an aspiring working-class amateur astronomer, who had to be at work at six o'clock in the morning, six days a week, and was lucky by 1870 to get Saturday afternoons off.

Without being in any way political, it can probably be said that the rapid growth of amateur astronomy since World War II is as much related to a more equitable distribution of wealth and a shortening of the working day as it is to a *real* fall in the prices of instruments and books. Astronomy, after all, is a subject which not only requires good-quality instruments to do it properly, but also the leisure to use them at peculiar hours and ponder over one's findings.

For the creation of this subject, which is far more than a mere hobby, therefore, we have many founding figures to thank. While we might admire the achievements of William Lassell and other 'Grand Amateurs' who did so much from their ample resources to advance astronomy in the Victorian age, we should perhaps reserve our profoundest respect for men like John Leech, whose love of the science gave him so much joy for next to nothing, and which he was so keen to pass on to his friends.

Acknowledgements

I wish to thank a number of astronomical societies around England for giving me information and supplying me with leads to local amateurs of the nineteenth century. I give especial thanks to Gerard Gilligan of the Liverpool, and Tony Cross of the Manchester Astronomical Societies. As I have worked on Victorian scientific archives over the years, a large number of amateur astronomers from that time have come to my notice. When I have completed my current biography of G. B. Airy, I plan upon writing a book about them.

References to John Leech come from the correspondence in the G. B. Airy Papers, now in Cambridge University Library, RGO 6/362-415.

Mr Tregent's large refracting telescope with which he gave 'penny a peep' lecture demonstrations of the heavens in the streets of London during the 1850s. From Henry Mayhew's London Labour and the London Poor *(4 vols, 1851–1862).*

Further reading

The British Astronomical Association, the first fifty years. B.A.A., London, 1948.

James Nasmyth, *An Autobiography.* Ed. Samuel Smiles, 1883.

Patrick Moore, *The astronomy of Birr Castle.* Birr, 1981.

Allan Chapman, 'William Lassell (1799–1880): Practitioner, Patron and "Grand Amateur" of Victorian Astronomy', *Vistas in Astronomy*, 32, pp. 341–70. 1989.

J. L. E. Dreyer, etc. (eds.), *History of the Royal Astronomical Society, 1820–1920*, 1923.

The History of the Manchester Astronomical Societies (UMIST, AVPU, Manchester, 1992)

For a guide to wages and prices in Victorian times, see John Burnett, *A history of the cost of living*, pp. 189–282. Pelican original, 1969.

New tools for the solar observer

DONALD F. TROMBINO

The British solar observer, William M. Baxter, working with modest equipment, produced remarkable results which he published in his 1963 classic work, *The Sun and the Amateur Astronomer*. It was written by an amateur astronomer specifically for other amateurs. Although it has long been out of print, it contains a plethora of valuable observing techniques, many of which are still used by today's active solar observers. It is well worth searching for in libraries or out-of-print book shops.

Dramatic advances in equipment have evolved over the ensuing thirty years. Modern solar observers routinely use over-the-aperture glass and mylar filters, solar prominence viewers, high-tech Hydrogen-alpha (H-α) and Calcium K-Line solar filter systems, video recorders, CCD equipment and new-generation ultra-fine grain films capable of capturing minute solar detail. All of these tools were either non-existent or solely within the realms (and budgets) of major solar observatories in Baxter's day. They are direct results of space exploration technology.

Numerous H-α filter systems are in daily use throughout the world, yet one is hard-pressed to find little more than cursory mention of them in any of the scores of popular books written especially for the amateur astronomer or astrophotographer. Although a growing number of 'night owl' observers have taken up H-α observing, there are but a handful who have any idea of their design features, advantages, limitations or applications. With the exception of an occasional article in magazines or journals written by self-taught experts, the amateur is left to experiment, and that can be dangerous in *this* branch of astronomy!

Advertisements are helpful, but seldom detailed. Product reviews are useful, but some magazines have shied away from them in recent months, fearing possible loss of advertising revenue should the review be less than totally favourable. Result – amateur solar observers find themselves in a frustrating quandary. The prospective buyer has little choice but to trust the advice of local dealers, which may or may not be reliable. Recently, the director of a major astronomical instrument supply house was puzzled as to why a H-α filter I was demonstrating cost much more than the full aperture 'white light' solar filters that his firm routinely sells every day! Obviously, an uninformed dealer cannot hope to educate the unwary buyer who cannot be expected to make an intelligent buying decision without all the facts. How does one cope with this dilemma?!

The true value of an item cannot be assessed unless one has a thorough understanding of what it is capable of doing: yet, most amateurs invariably inquire first about price. Budget is, indeed, an important consideration, but one must not lose sight of the fact that the days of simplicity are gone in today's high-tech marketplace.

Figure 1. The author at the controls of his 6-inch (15.2 cm) solar telescope. (Photo: Cliff Gosney)

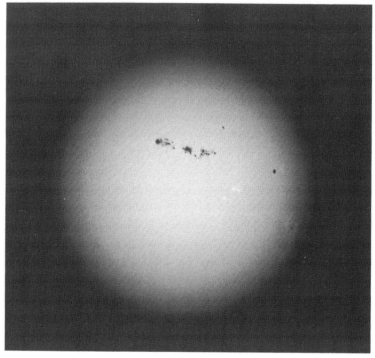

Figure 2. White-light photo of Sun showing complex sunspot groups, limb darkening, and faculæ in the Sun's photosphere using 76-mm, f/16 refractor with N.D.4 full aperture filter at 1/250 sec. on TP-2415 (ISO-100) film. July 12, 1992, 1320 UT. (Photo: D. Trombino)

My enthusiasm for solar observing spans more than thirty-five years. During that time I have experimented with a variety of accessories and photographic techniques. Hopefully, the tools described here will stimulate your interest and encourage you to expand your observing horizons. My purpose is not to recommend one product over another, but rather to briefly describe some of the latest accessories so that you will be able to ask the right questions, and thereby make the logical choice in terms of the extent of your interest and budget. At the same time I hope astrophotographers will find my techniques and exposure tips helpful.

Many of these tools have been performance tested using the

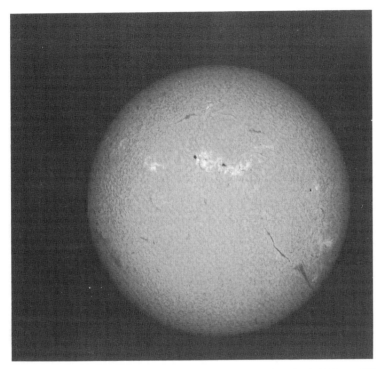

Figure 3. H-α 'filtergram' taken moments after Figure 2, with author's 15.2-cm, f/12 refractor, with 60-mm ERF at f/30.4, 1828-mm focal length. A DayStar 0.7Å 'ATM' H-α filter was used to reveal dramatic chromospheric details invisible in white-light filter. Note plage areas around sunspots, filaments and solar granulation. (Photo: D. Trombino)

6-inch (15.2-cm) refractor in my Davis Memorial Solar Observatory (Figure 1).

White light solar filters

By far the safest means of observing the Sun is to project its image on to a white surface, suitably shielded by means of a simple projection box or similar device. This will enhance contrast and bring out details in sunspot structure, limb darkening, and faculæ; features confined to the Sun's photosphere (Figure 2).

Advanced solar observers usually prefer to view or photograph the Sun directly. Various means have been used to safely reduce the focused rays of the Sun, including dark pieces of absorptive glass filters placed in or over the eyepieces of small, imported refractors sold in department stores. These have proved to be very dangerous, and often crack due to the Sun's concentrated rays. If you own such filters **throw them out!**

Many excellent articles, by experienced solar observers, have been written about the features revealed in telescopes equipped with properly used, safe filters. Peter J. Garbett's 'Observing the Sun' in the *1980 Yearbook of Astronomy* is a fine example.

Over-the-aperture glass and mylar filters have proven to be a safe alternative for beginners and advanced amateur solar observers, provided they are purchased from well-established, reputable manufacturers or their dealers. Within the past year, or so, certain solar filters have been advertised in the UK as being suitable for refractors, when in fact, they are not! Although they may appear to have low transmission in the visible part of the solar spectrum, tests have shown they pass a high percentage of hazardous invisible radiation. *Caveat emptor!*

Prior to buying *any* white-light solar filter I recommend reading an informative article on the subject, 'Safe Solar Filters' by B. Ralph Chu, *Sky & Telescope*, Vol. 62, No. 2, August 1981, pp. 119–21, for proper guidelines.

Observing the Sun differs from night-time viewing. Deep-sky objects, many light years distant, require large apertures to gather and bring to a focus their dim light and fuzzy features. Paradoxically, smaller apertures are far better suited to daytime observations, because they are less troubled by air turbulence that commonly interferes with solar observations. A 2-inch (5-cm) refractor, for example, will reveal a wealth of ever-changing detail on our nearest star, and a telescope of 4 to 6 inches (10 cm to 15 cm) aperture is capable of serious research provided commonsense precautions are taken.

Never attempt solar observations without properly filtered and positioned equipment under the guidance of an experienced solar observer, and, under no circumstances, leave such equipment unattended. Securely cover finder scopes or, better still, remove them altogether. They are <u>not</u> needed.

Having said that, I must add that solar observing is, without question, one of the most rewarding and exhilarating experiences awaiting the amateur astronomer. Even during periods of low sunspot activity, when the Sun appears featureless in white-light filters, observers using H-α filters are treated to a solar show comparable to viewing creation in the making in real time! The difference is like night and day as Figures 2 and 3 clearly show.

Energy rejection filters (ERFs)

Energy Rejection pre-filters, unlike the inconel-coated glass and mylar white-light filters which reflect the Sun's rays, allow the light to pass through them, but cut out more than 80 per cent of the harmful ultraviolet and infrared radiation 'before' it reaches the delicate H-α filter, where it can bleach its protective coatings. The blocking elements within the H-α filter, itself, eliminate the small percentage of potentially hazardous radiation, while allowing only a very narrow band centred on the H-α line at 6562.8Å (Ångströms) to pass through to the telescope eyepiece or camera. They must **never** be used without the H-α filter firmly in place and secured to the eyepiece focuser.

Ideally, the wave-front error of the light passed by the ERF must not exceed one-quarter wave at 6565Å. Typically they are made of finely polished red optical glass comparable to Schott RG-610. These optical windows help to increase contrast while sufficiently reducing telescope aperture to give the observer a nominal f/30 focal ratio. This long effective focal length also helps to create a 'parallel' beam which the H-α filter requires in order to function properly. Typically, a 4-inch (10-cm) f/15 refractor requires a 2-inch (5-cm) ERF to create a f/30 beam. Short focus refractors (e.g. f/5– f/6) need a Barlow lens and/or correcting lens system positioned 'in front of' the H-α filter. Failure to use an ERF with H-α filters could ultimately result in a very costly repair job!

Lumicon solar prominence filter

W. M. Baxter may have had in mind something akin to Lumicon's Solar Prominence Filter when he wrote:

'. . . I can only look forward to the time when a simple and inexpensive piece of coloured glass, or other material, will be available to cut out all the wavelengths except the H-α line of the solar spectrum when applied to the amateur's ordinary refracting or reflecting telescope.'

Unfortunately, affordable H-α filter systems, as we know them today, did not become commercially available to the amateur until 1973, three years after Baxter's death.

Among the low-cost units is Lumicon's Prominence Filter, but, as its name implies, its 1.5Å bandpass will show little more than solar prominences. Its compact size makes it ideal for use with virtually any type of telescope, including Newtonian reflectors. Adapters are available for 2-inch, 1.25-inch, and 0.965-inch eyepieces. The manufacturer suggests reducing the size of one's telescope aperture enough to create an f/20 focal ratio, but I have found that stopping my scope down so as to produce an f/30 focal ratio gave a much better (and perhaps safer) view. Since this is not a very narrow bandpass subångström filter it is not affected by normal temperature changes. However, like all H-α filters, it must be protected with a red ERF.

A small plastic tuning knob 'tilts' the filter slightly within its housing in order to centre it on the H-α line. It is primarily a visual accessory, although simple 'filtergrams' (b&w photos taken through monochromatic 'one-colour' filters) are possible with a bit of trial and error experimenting. The resulting print will show 'prominences only' around an otherwise featureless solar disk. Visually, however, sunspots, bright faculæ or plages and perhaps a 'filament' (prominences silhouetted against the solar disk) can be detected under favourable seeing conditions. For æsthetics one might wish to do some darkroom masking to block out the stark white disk. Clear, dark blue skies are a must, since atmospheric haze will drastically reduce contrast and all but obliterate even prominence detail.

Its moderate cost is comparable to a good SLR camera. With that in mind, the low budget, casual observer willing to overlook its obvious limitations, may wish to consider this solar observing tool.

Baader Planetarium 10Å (H-α Coronagraph) prominence viewer

The Sun's corona or 'outer atmosphere' is over one-million times fainter than the light emitted by its photosphere. It can only be glimpsed in its full splendour during the fleeting moments of a total solar eclipse, when the Moon completely masks the solar disk. Attempts to artificially duplicate this natural phenomenon have frustrated scientists since the 1870s.

The French astronomer, Bernard Lyot, succeeded where others had failed, and in 1930 announced that he was able to detect the innermost portions of the corona using a modified telescope of his design. His coronagraph consisted of a simple 8-cm plano-convex objective (achromatic or APO objectives are not needed when observing in monochromatic light), a series of light baffles to reduce glare, an occulting disk to simulate the Moon, a field lens to focus the solar image, an adjustable iris diaphragm to further reduce scattered light, and a transfer lens which achromatized, enlarged, and refocused the combined cone disk and solar image to create an artificial eclipse similar to that shown in Figure 4.

He later improved his system with the addition of a monochromatic, quartz-polaroid filter (Figure 5), and by 1938 he was able to view the Sun's prominences, as well. Despite his best efforts, he was unable to capture the outer regions of the corona. The culprit was dust in the Earth's atmosphere and within the coronagraph itself. To eliminate dust and scattered light, Lyot coated the interior of his coronagraph with sticky grease, and rubbed 'nose oil' (a combination of human sweat and body oil) over his telescope's objective!

Even today, the best Earth-based coronagraphs, perched atop tall mountain peaks, are incapable of revealing coronal details beyond two solar radii. During natural solar eclipses an observer can easily detect the corona to a distance of five, six or more solar radii.

Since World War II scores of amateurs and professionals have designed and built similar devices, among them H. E. Dall of England, and in Germany Prof. Otto Nögel of Landshut and Wolfgang Lille of Hamburg. Lille's unique, four-section coronagraph, manufactured by the Baader Planetarium KG, incorporates many of Lyot's features (thankfully, without the grease or nose oil!). However, his device will not reveal the inner or outer corona, and in this respect the term 'Coronagraph' is a bit of a misnomer. In fairness, it must be said, it was not designed for this purpose. Instead, when properly mounted to a suitable refractor, it reveals absolutely stunning views of prominences that originate in the Sun's chromosphere and sometimes extend into its lower corona. The viewer sees an annular eclipse with brilliant prominences projected against the pitch blackness of space.

Baader manufactures 4Å and 10Å models centred on the 6563Å (656.3nm – 'nanometre' = one thousand-millionth or 10^{-9} of a metre) H-α line of the solar spectrum. These broad passband filters are not nearly narrow enough to reveal H-α disk features, but that is of no matter since the Sun's disk is completely masked.

Figure 4. Spectacular solar prominences on 5 June 1992 were dramatically recorded on TP-2415 film using a Baader Planetarium Prominence Coronagraph fitted to an 80mm refractor. (Photo: Werner Baumann)

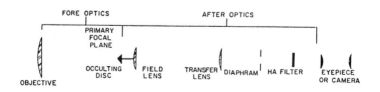

Figure 5. Diagram showing the typical layout of a Lyot Coronagraph. (D. Trombino)

The Baader Prominence Viewer comes with a kit consisting of six cone rings, marked and sized to match the apparent diameter of the Sun at different times of the year. Tweezers and gloves are also included. They must be used when inserting, removing or adjusting the disks or the coronagraph's internal optics. **Caution!** They receive the 'direct' focused rays of the Sun and can get very hot! Temperatures of 140°F (60°C) are not unusual. The gloves prevent skin oil contact with the field or relay lenses. The same annoying dust that plagued Lyot's system can lower image contrast, and an unluckily placed dust speck on the field lens might mimic the appearance of a prominence!

This instrument was originally designed only for use with Celestron's Firstscope 80 or the Vixen 80mm, f/910 refractor. Obviously, this severely limited its usefulness. Fortunately, for many amateurs, it has been re-designed so that it can now be used with refractors having 810-mm to 1000-mm focal lengths. Custom viewers are also available for longer focal length telescopes. The manufacturer asserts that an ERF is not necessary when the viewer is used with 80-mm or smaller refractors. Larger scopes must add this feature.

The Baader Prominence Viewer has been popular on the Continent for several years where it has gained wide acceptance. The 10Å model is now available to North American solar observers through Astro-Physics, a highly respected manufacturer of top of the line apochromatic refractors. It can now be used on 'any' of their telescopes. Baader recommends their 'Eudiascopic' eyepieces, but any standard 1.25-inch parfocal eyepiece will do.

The manufacturer has recently introduced its 'VIP Excenter' which permits one to scan around the circumference of the Sun's disk with high-power eyepieces, and home in on a specific prominence for a close-up view. It accepts standard 1.25-inch or 2-inch eyepieces, any SLR camera with the proper T-adapter, or the Celestron Binocular Viewer for a simulated 3D view. The VIP Excenter is an optional accessory, at additional cost from Baader, but is included as standard with the Astro-Physics package.

On the positive side, the Baader Prominence Viewer allows full aperture solar observations of prominences. Its H-α filter is fully blocked from X-ray to the ultraviolet, and from above the H-α region to the deep infrared wavelengths. Its 40 to 50 per cent transmission enhances prominence features. It does not need electrical power or heat stabilization, and is not affected by temperature changes because it is not a sub-Ångström filter.

Its negative points should also be considered. It needs 'perfect' polar alignment which can be a bit tricky during daylight hours. A sturdy equatorial mount with 'solar rate' tracking is essential in order to keep the occulted solar disk safely hidden from view. Except as noted, it is not readily interchangeable with other refractors. If you plan to use it with other refractors you will need a complete new set of occulting disks for each focal length. That is a consideration should you decide to sell it in future. It cannot easily be used with long-focus refractors exceeding 1500 mm focal length. The Prominence Viewer must be kept scrupulously clean and dust-free at all times. Viewing is limited to thirty minutes at any given time, after which the telescope must be turned away from the Sun in order to give the filter's optics a 'cooling off' period. Extreme care must be taken when changing the occulting disks. Remember, a partially occulted disk is uncomfortably bright. Generally speaking, the Sun's largest apparent diameter occurs in January when the Earth is closest to it. It is smallest in July when we are farthest from it. Selecting the correct diameter disk may be a trial and error exercise, at first, and so the Sun's bright disk may not be totally covered. Should this happen **minimize the time you look at it. Hide the Sun behind the occulting disk as quickly as possible!** This is a precision scientific instrument intended for use by experienced solar observers, who would be well-advised to read and follow carefully the hazard warnings that are included with the Prominence Viewer.

Sub-Ångström H-α solar filters

Sub-Ångström, ultra-narrow band H-α filters are far more complex than the filter systems already described. They consist of multiple layers of space-age optical interference filters, with coatings only a few microns thick, in sandwich-like sections called 'etalons' (Fr. standard of measurement). These precision filters are literally made one at a time, and quality tested at several crucial stages during the production process. Naturally, they are costly. They are designed to reject all but a very narrow slice of the Sun's spectrum centred at 6562.8Å (Ångströms), a wavelength at which hydrogen atoms emit visible light. Viewing the Sun at this ultra-narrow H-α wavelength reveals details impossible to see with standard, low cost, white-light filters that simply dim the Sun across the entire spectrum or continuum. (See Figure 11 on page 199.)

With them we are able to view or photograph brilliant solar flares, filaments, super-granulations, spicules, plage areas, and active magnetic lines in the Sun's chromosphere. Eric H. Strach's superb article 'Observing the Sun in Hydrogen-alpha' clearly describes these, and other solar phenomena in the *1986 Yearbook*. Since this relatively thin portion of the Sun's atmosphere consists mainly of ionized hydrogen, the observer is rewarded with a constantly changing view quite unlike anything visible in white-light filters (see Figure 3).

DayStar 'T-Scanner' H-α filters

The name DayStar needs no introduction to experienced solar observers. Its founder and president, Del. N. Woods, launched his career during the early days of the Space Age. Since then he has produced a steady stream of H-α filter systems which are second to none in terms of affordability, quality, and dependability. His superb filters are used at major observatories, educational institutions, aboard NASA space missions, and by an ever-increasing number of amateur astronomers around the world. He does not advertise because he does not have to. Through reputation alone, he has done more to advance amateur solar observing than anyone else in recent memory. All DayStar filters carry a full, five-year warranty.

The T-Scanner (tilt scanner) is designed for general sub-Ångström observations of the Sun. The original 0.9Å T-Scanner has been superseded with 0.8Å, 0.7Å, 0.6Å and an ultra-narrow 0.5Å model. One-half ångström tilt-type filters were unheard of only a few short years ago! As one gently adjusts its thumb screw, the filter's passband or 'fringe' scans across the solar image. Since all tilt-type, ultra-narrowband, interference filters shift quickly towards the shorter wavelengths when tilted, you will rarely require more than one turn of the thumb screw to scan the Sun. T-Scanner line is designed to operate throughout the 0°C to 40°C ambient temperature range. The warmer conditions are, the more tilt is required, and vice versa. Buyers should specify their local ambient temperatures when ordering because a filter that has been calibrated for a chilly Toronto winter will not perform to specifications in the summer-like climate of Tampa, for example. That problem is about to change. DayStar has developed a simple heating/cooling accessory for these filters.

The T-Scanner's 1.18-inch (30-mm) clear aperture allows full H-α disk viewing. It is designed to be used with refractors or Schmidt Cassegrain Telescopes (SCTs). Newtonian telescope users would have to modify their scopes in order to accommodate the filter's 2-inch (50-mm) thickness. Buyers should advise DayStar of the make, model and/or outside diameter of their telescope to ensure receiving a properly sized ERF lens cover. Adapters are available for either 1.25-inch or 2-inch eyepieces. These filters are provided with mounting flanges that are threaded to accept standard Celestron or Meade eyepiece visual back assemblies or SLR camera threaded T-adapters. DayStar does not normally supply T-Adapters since they are readily available at major camera sales outlets or local telescope dealers.

Although these are precision-made instruments there is nothing esoteric about using them visually or photographically. Their simplicity, compactness, and light weight (about 16 oz/0.453 kg) have made them extremely popular with a growing number of 'on the go' amateurs, as well as educators.

DayStar 'ATM' and University series H-α filters

DayStar's 'ATM' model filters are fabricated with instrument quality components, and will meet the needs of most amateur solar observers. They are perfect for high contrast visual or photographic applications; however, they require standard (110 V, AC 60 Hz) household current for temperature stabilization. If used outside the USA a transformer must be used. A moderately priced 12 V inverter is about to be introduced by Edwin Hirsch that will enable *all* ATM and University filters to be used in the field.

If your primary interests are prices and prominences, but you also want to know what's happening on the Sun, DayStar's 0.8Å 'ATM' filter will do the job nicely. I've used one for over eighteen very enjoyable years without any problems.

The 0.7Å filter is a fine intermediate choice. Red prominences stand out briskly, and disk features have good contrast. My 0.7Å 'ATM' filter was used to take many of the dramatic filtergrams that appear in this article. It is an excellent choice for general work and as a teaching aid.

DayStar's 0.6Å 'ATM' filter provides excellent contrast and is ideal for detailed studies of active solar regions. Prominences are still quite evident visually and photographically.

Finally, the 0.5Å filter reveals superb disk features, although prominences are subdued. When used with telescopes capable of producing one arcsecond resolution, the results are comparable to those obtained at large solar observatories.

It is important to note that the bandpasses indicated are maximum. Whichever filter you order will most likely be somewhat better, as the manufacturer is conservative in this regard; a big plus for you! In my experience I have never had to wait more than fifteen to twenty minutes for my filters to stabilize. When specified, the 'ATM' and University models are furnished with an adjustable temperature-regulating hand control box. With it the observer can minutely adjust temperatures and thereby observe and photograph absorption and emission features in both the upper and lower parts of the solar chromosphere. To see photospheric or continuum details simply unplug the filter from its power source. The manufacturer will shortly announce a new series of ATM and University 'T-scanner' filters with tiltable filter elements for Doppler shift experiments.

DayStar's University models are hand-fabricated with the highest filtering components available today. They are designed to meet or exceed the needs of the most discriminating observer and professional institutions. These state-of-the-art filters are pricey, yet affordable enough to be purchased with discretionary funds as opposed to hard-to-come-by grant money.

Calcium K-line solar filters

Located in the deep blue/violet region of the solar spectrum is the Ca-K line, centred at 3933.7Å. Viewing the Sun in the light of ionized calcium is a unique experience, and one seldom available to the amateur solar observer until now.

One indication of strong magnetic solar activity is the presence of plages (Fr. for 'beaches') which usually appear before the formation of sunspots, and remain long after they have vanished.

Plages normally appear as broad areas of intensified brightness in the H-α and many other wavelengths. In Ca-K light these brighter areas roughly coincide with the enhanced vertical magnetic fields that surround sunspots in the photosphere. They have been called by several names which may seem a bit confusing at first. For example, when seen in white light, usually in the limb darkened areas of the Sun, they are called 'faculæ' or 'flocculi', but when observed in Calcium light or in Hydrogen-α in the Sun's chromospheric region, they are known as 'plages' or bright flocculi.

DayStar now offers the amateur two basic Calcium K-Line filters: a 2.0Å single cavity model for high contrast solar disk features, and a 6.0Å, four cavity, square head filter which I prefer

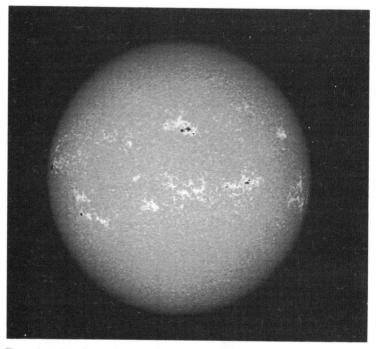

Figure 6. Active plage regions stand out against the mottled solar disk in this Calcium K-line filtergram. The author used a DayStar 6.0Å Ca K filter centred at 3933.7Å on Kodak TP–2415 film with a 1/250-sec. exposure at f/27.5 on October 5, 1992. The film was processed in Kodak D-19 developer at 68°F for 4 min.

because it also reveals (albeit with difficulty) brighter 'Quiescent' prominences which are closely associated with plage. These 'quiet' features (as opposed to highly active short-lived, flare-related prominences) can last several solar rotations, and often attain considerable lengths (i.e. 400,000 kilometres, or more!).

Outwardly these filters resemble the T-Scanner, and like its H-α cousin, one centres on the broad Ca K-line by gently turning a small knob to tilt the filter. Heating is not required because it is not a sub-Ångström filter. Nor does it require an ERF since, unlike H-α filters, its coatings do not easily bleach. The objectives of most telescopes will have to be reduced to produce a nominal f/30 focal ratio.

My initial impression of this filter was not favourable because, much to my surprise, I could barely make out the solar disk. The image was so dark that I had difficulty in focusing on the clear glass screen of my SLR despite using a deep rubber eye cup. Undaunted, I covered my head and camera body with a black towel in order to adapt my eyes to the dark. After a short time, my eyes became adjusted sufficiently so that I was able to obtain a sharp focus (Figure 6). I do not recommend this procedure to those living in hot climates, unless one enjoys 'facial saunas'! The Calcium K-line is located in a very dark region of the solar spectrum, beyond the normal visual perception of some individuals. To find an alternative to my black towel, I found that a positive lens similar to those used in tele-compressors, placed 'after' the Ca-K filter, reduced image size but increased image brightness by a factor of four times. Of course, a CCD image intensifier will also do the job quite nicely if one can afford this luxury. A standard 8-mm one lux home camcorder is a good alternative.

Advanced solar observers and educational institutions wishing to expand their solar observing or educational programmes will find this filter costs little more than DayStar's 0.6Å 'ATM' H-α filter; a comparatively small investment when one considers the added educational dividends it offers.

Solaris H-α telescope system

A growing number of first-rate telescope manufacturers, anxious to tap into this market, have jumped on the bandwagon. Tele Vue Optics (now of Suffern, New York) was among the first to do so. Their Solaris H-α Telescope System is unique in many ways. Realizing the need for a compact H-α solar telescope, Al Nagler, president of Tele Vue Optics, designed his Solaris Telescope System around DayStar's 0.7Å T-Scanner filter. This instrument has been popularized by Edwin Hirsch of Tomkins Cove, New York.

The Solaris features a 60-mm, f/9 multi-coated, cemented achromatic objective lens which is more than adequate for viewing the Sun in monochromatic light. A 58-mm red ERF is mounted directly in front of the objective. It is slightly tilted to help ward off unwanted ghost reflections. To achieve an optimum f/30 parallel beam, Tele Vue combined a specially designed corrector lens with its 'Big Barlow' lens, and coupled it with precisely spaced extension tubes to the T-Scanner, and a 2-inch mirror diagonal eyepiece holder. This combination boosts the f/9 primary beam to the required 1750 mm focal length. According to its maker, the optical

Figure 7. Central Florida amateur, Ernie Sangraw, prepares to take a full-disk patrol filtergram of the sun, in H-α light using the Solaris Telescope System mounted to the author's 15.2-cm solar refractor. (Photo: D. Trombino)

system provides a flat, diffraction-limited field more than one degree in diameter.

Without dependence upon electrical power, the Solaris is so portable that it can be taken around the corner or around the world, and set up in minutes. This is a real bonus to 'eclipse chasers' anxious to view surface detail as well as prominence activity before and after totality.

Keeping the Sun centred within the field of view is not a problem, since the solar disk is visible at all times. The tube assembly, only 25 inches (0.634 m) long, easily fits within the overhead storage areas of most aircraft. The entire system weighs only 10 pounds (4.8 kg) and comes complete in a fitted, soft carrying case with shoulder strap, very similar to carry-on luggage.

I have tested this instrument extensively and found that it gives remarkably good images. Since it is normally sold without a tripod or mount of any kind, I mounted it piggyback to my observatory refractor (Figure 7). Its L-shaped configuration was somewhat awkward and required re-balancing my larger telescope. It also positioned Solaris's eyepiece too far from the eyepiece of my comparison filter which was mounted to the main telescope. To overcome this minor problem, I removed Tele Vue's 2-inch mirror diagonal, and used the Solaris in what has come to be known as its 'photographic' or 'straight-through' configuration. This gave me a brighter, f/27.5 image which was fine for visual or photographic use.

Solaris is furnished with a Tele Vue 40-mm Plössl eyepiece which yields a comfortable 44×full-disk view. Optional eyepieces are available, but I found a 20-mm eyepiece is about the useful limit. Shorter focus eyepieces will only dim the image. Tele Vue's standard rubber eye cup was not sufficient to keep out annoying stray light. A deeper cup solved that minor flaw.

The Solaris does a fine job for its intended purpose, but it is a 'dedicated' system, designed solely for H-α solar observations. Despite its rather steep price tag, the Solaris is an excellent choice for budget-minded public observatories and planetariums as well as for serious amateurs or those with Newtonian reflectors who might consider piggybacking it.

Tele Vue Genesis f/30 solar kit

Observers who wish to have the Sun in the morning and the Moon at night can now do so using the same basic components used in the Solaris telescope. Tele Vue has recently introduced its f/30 Genesis Solar Kit which converts this excellent 'deep sky' f/5 fast focus, fluorite optical system into a long focus, f/30 solar telescope. I've tested this system using Tele Vue's very sturdy 'Gibraltar' altazimuth mount and easily recorded dramatic solar activity on August 17, 1992 (Figure 8). Solar tracking with this system is unnecessary since these 'solar snapshots' are obtained with exposures on the order of 1/125 sec. on Kodak TP-2415 (ISO-100) b&w ultra fine-grain pan film. Prominences are easily recorded with exposures of about one-half to one-quarter second. A word of caution to those Genesis telescope users who use Tele Vue's 'Starbeam' or 'Red Star' projection finder. Remove it! It is unnecessary, and could pose a serious hazard. Use the shadow cast by the telescope to locate the Sun. Like the Solaris, it easily fits into the overhead storage areas of most aircraft.

Astro-Physics Solar System Kit

Astro-Physics is about to introduce its new Solar System Kit which is similar in many ways to Tele Vue's Genesis Kit. The Solar System can be used on 'any' Astro-Physics refractor, including their

Figure 8. A Class B-1 importance Solar Flare was recorded near a large sunspot (centre) on August 17, 1992 at 1834UT with a 1/125-sec. exposure on Kodak TP-2415 tech. pan film using the Tele Vue Genesis f/30 Solar Kit. (Photo: D. Trombino)

105 Traveler EDT, 130 StarFire EDT, and Star 12ED (155, 180) model apochromatic (APO) refractors.

The kit incorporates the standard multi-coated Barlow and their 'Telecentric' Unit which is needed to form a parallel beam. Naturally, the kit includes an adapter for any of DayStar's line of H-α filters. When used with Astro-Physics refractors up to 130-mm aperture, a full-sized ERF can be used, thus reducing exposures to fractions of a second to freeze fleeting solar phenomena such as flares and extremely active prominences. Of course, fast exposures greatly reduce the adverse affects of atmospheric turbulence, and thereby assure sharper images. These kits are also suited for use with 94-mm and 130-mm Brandon refractors.

Figure 9. DayStar's system used to obtain the solar flare filter gram shown in Figure 10. (Photo: D. Trombino)

In reality, these systems are not new. Similar devices were quietly introduced by DayStar Filter Corp. several years ago (Figure 9). The cover illustration and Figure 10 were obtained using one of these early kits. DayStar utilizes a specially designed minus 12, negative singlet lens, made of heat-resistant BK-47 optical glass, since it was found that 'some' cemented achromatic Barlow lenses have a tendency to 'fog' when subjected to prolonged periods of ultraviolet solar radiation. Of course, DayStar's Barlow lens is not achromatic. It does not have to be, because colour corrected optics are unnecessary for monochromatic solar observing or photography. I learned this one evening when I attempted to show Venus to a group of advanced students. I forgot to replace my DayStar solar Barlow lens with my planetary achromatic Barlow. Much to my embarrassment, we were all treated to a colourful spectrum of the planet!

These are but a few of the exciting new tools available to modern solar observers. More marvels, never imagined by W. M. Baxter,

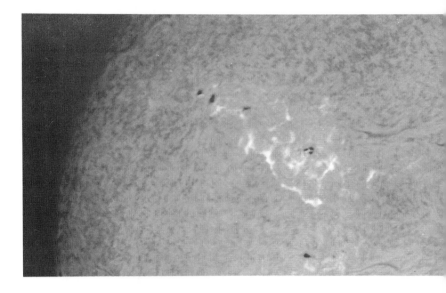

Figure 10. The author recorded one of the most active Solar Flares in the current sunspot cycle on June 10, 1991 at 0228UT. It spanned over 27 degrees square on the solar disk and was responsible for a colourful aurora. Note filaments, sunspots plage and granulation in this one-arcsecond filtergram. (Photo: D. Trombino)

are yet to come, as cutting-edge technology produces new accessories, currently on the drawing boards or in the development stages. I am convinced that when placed in the right hands, they will enable the dedicated amateur to contribute valuable data to the professional astronomical community. They will also serve to educate tomorrow's scientists in a way that no textbook could ever possibly hope to.

The American jazz singer, Al Jolson, once said: 'You ain't seen nothin' yet!' How right he was!

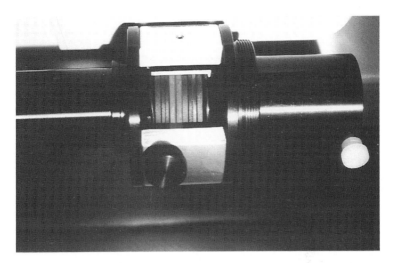

Figure 11. This sectioned DayStar H-α filter was fabricated under very high vacuum conditions using sophisticated electronic and optical monitoring instrumentation. The filter pack consists of (Right to Left) an anti-reflection coated window, a narrow-band blocking filter, an etalon window, a Fabry-Perot solid spacer crystal, another etalon window, a broadband trimming filter and finally an anti-reflection coated window. The T-Scanner filter, shown above, eliminates all solar energy except an ultra-narrow passband centered on the hydrogen Balmer-alpha spectral line at 6562.8Å. Note the black filter pack tilting knob used to center the etalons on this narrow line. (Photo: D. Trombino)

Recommended Reading

Books

Baxter, W. M., *The Sun and the Amateur Astronomer*. W. W. Norton & Co. Inc., New York, 1963 (2nd revised edition, David and Charles, Newton Abbot, 1973).

Garbett, Peter J., 'Observing the Sun', in *1980 Yearbook of Astronomy*, Patrick Moore, Ed. Sidgwick & Jackson Ltd., London and W. W. Norton & Co. Inc., New York.

Hill, Richard, Ed., *The New Observe and Understand the Sun: A Program for Observing and Photographing the Sun*, Astronomical League, Science Service Building, 1719 N. Street N.W., Washington, D.C. 1990. (Contains numerous articles by well-known white light and H-α solar observers.)

Strach, Eric H., 'Observing the Sun in Hydrogen-Alpha' *1986 Yearbook of Astronomy*, Patrick Moore, Ed., Sidgwick & Jackson Ltd., London and W. W. Norton & Co. Inc., New York.

Veio, Fredrick N., *The Spectrohelioscope*, pub. privately 1991 by Fredrick N. Veio, P.O. Box 467, Clearlake Park, Calif. 95424, USA. (Contains detailed plans for construction and use of a spectrohelioscope, but includes information on H-α solar features and solar spectrum.)

Future Amateur Astronomy Today

LEIF J. ROBINSON

Those who do not want the future should think it over. In saying no to progress, it is not the future that they condemn, but themselves. –
VICTOR HUGO.

My title might seem perplexing, but it shouldn't be. It means exactly what it says – the future is *now*. The future is also *digital* – computer-controlled telescopes, charge-coupled-device (CCD) detectors, image-processing programs, and enormous data bases.

Amateur astronomy is no longer defined by improvements in hardware, whether for performance or convenience. Nor is it confined to traditional activities such as astrophotography or the visual observation of the Moon, planets, and variable stars. An electronic revolution that set the agenda for 'tetchy' amateurs a decade ago has now trickled down to ordinary consumers. The solid-state circuitry hidden in the drive of your commercial tele-scope is almost certainly more sophisticated than state-of-the-art controllers a decade ago.

Computer-assisted telescopes (CATs), when combined with other technological wonders, have the potential to raise the popu-larity of amateur astronomy to heights it has never seen. No, our hobby will not overtake golf, but it should grow dramatically over the next decade thanks to these remarkable devices. Affordable technology already allows amateurs to do many things that profes-sionals a decade ago barely dreamed of. In fact, the technology gap between amateurs and professionals is actually shrinking in many arenas.

Amateurs are entering a new age – the era of *computer-as-observatory*. Since computers mean software, let's look at a recent product that does just about everything and introduces many topics that will be discussed below. *Epoch 2000* (produced by Farpoint Research in Downey, California) allows you to plot 45,000 stars, 13,000 deep-sky objects, 7,700 asteroids, and 650 comets! If that isn't enough, and your computer is hooked up to a device that plays CD-ROMs (compact discs with read-only memory), you can add

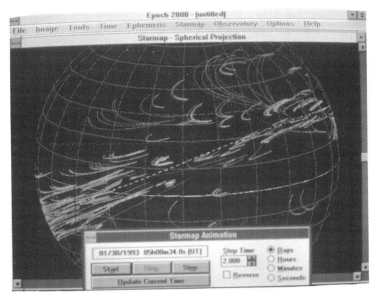

Figure 1. Among its many capabilities, Epoch 2000.0 *software plots star charts and tracks comets and asteroids. In this image the motions of some 300 comets are depicted.* (Courtesy Farpoint Research)

fifteen million stars from the Hubble *Guide Star Catalog* (available from NASA for only about $50).

This software for IBM-compatible personal computers also allows you to manipulate or 'process' images – either ones taken with your CCD camera or ones you acquired. One spectacular example of off-the-shelf imagery is *Mission To Mars: Digital Image Map*, produced by the US Geological Survey and available at about the same price as the Hubble catalogue. Its 2,394 frames each cover an area roughly 200 miles square and faithfully depict topographical and brightness features. Of course, if you don't like what you see on the screen, you can process the image to change its colour, contrast, or whatever!

Finally, *Epoch 2000* allows you to control the LX-200 automatic telescope by Meade and a CCD camera. There are even plans to connect users of this software to a remote telescope network. Then you won't even need your own instrument; all you will have to do is join the network for access to the entire sky!

As will be described below, these and other ideas are not fanciful; they are very real and already moving forward at a dizzy and accelerating pace. Come, join me on a wild ride into the future of amateur astronomy!

Fright in Eden

For some, the future may be unsettling. I see three major impediments to the wholehearted, explosive adoption of new technology.

1. High-tech equipment is expensive. An 8-inch CAT from Celestron or Meade, one that can point itself to any object you choose, sells for perhaps twice that of its 'dumb' cousin. When a CCD detector (such as the ST-6 from Santa Barbara Instrument Group) and accompanying computer are added, the cost may double again. You'd better be prepared to write a $7,000 cheque. Yet, from now on, when amateurs think of buying or building a new telescope, they would be wise to budget an equal amount for a CCD detector and the computer needed to run it.

2. Since most amateurs are not computer or electronic whizzes, they may doubt the utility of new-fangled techno-toys and the power these gadgets could place, literally, at their fingertips. The best cure for such scepticism is a good dose of unbiased, first-hand experience, preferably in partnership with someone who has already taken the plunge off the technological dock!

3. Perhaps the biggest barrier to a thorough digital revolution is an æsthetic one. Does the adoption of a high-tech telescope or CCD detector sever some mystical connection to the sky? When an image appears on a TV screen rather than in an eyepiece, is an observer suddenly divorced from his or her forebears? Is that person somehow diminished? Of course, there is no universal answer to these questions. In fact, even a consensus opinion is unlikely – at least until light pollution becomes so bad that traditional observing simply becomes impossible!

The cost of technology troubles me particularly, because it threatens to create two classes of amateurs. On the one hand, there may well be 'haves' who make spectacular observations, hone the cutting edge of the hobby, and get their work published in

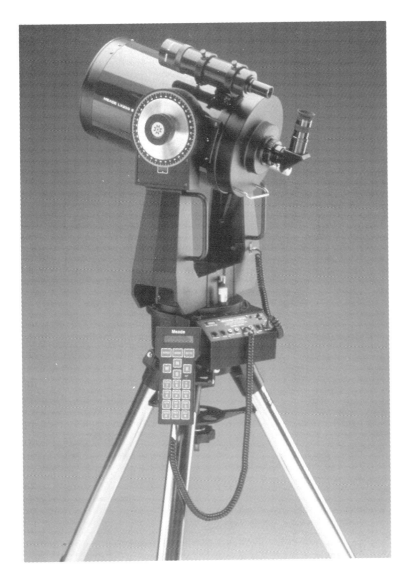

Figure 2. This recently introduced LX-200 8-inch Schmidt-Cassegrain is unique among portable computer-controlled telescopes because it can operate as an altazimuth, as shown here. (Courtesy Meade Instruments Corporation)

professional journals and popular magazines. On the other hand, 'have-nots' might become discouraged and abandon observing for armchair astronomy or give up the hobby altogether.

As in life, financial imbalances have always existed in amateur astronomy. Yet, during the next decade, the gap between the two classes has the potential for becoming wider than ever before. Until the mid-1980s, the largest amateur telescope could gather perhaps ten times more light than commonplace instruments. But that 'big gun' had an aperture three times larger and thus suffered from blurring by Earth's atmosphere. So some of its raw power was lost, and little telescopes could successfully compete. They could even excel in many areas, especially those demanding superb image sharpness or high contrast.

But when a CCD enters the picture, the scales always tip in favour of whomsoever possesses it – the telescope, in effect, becomes an accessory to the detector! Having a light-collecting efficiency of 40 per cent or more (film has about 2 per cent), a CCD turns a garden telescope into a giant. And if you just happen to have a giant, you can do what once required Palomar's power! It's a win-win situation!

As to the second impediment, people's fears of astroelectronics should quickly go away as gadgets become ever more user-friendly – just as the computer revolution blossomed once software became sophisticated and standardized. For an astronomical precedent, consider the highly specialized field of amateur photoelectric photometry. In the 1970s there were only a handful of practitioners. But after commercial, solid-state photometers were introduced in the 1980s, the International Amateur-Professional Photoelectric Photometry group began to grow rapidly and now has over 1,100 members.

The third item is inscrutable. I'm sure many amateurs would gladly toss rocks at self-pointing telescopes. 'Where's the fun of the hunt?' they ask. 'What about the satisfaction in gaining the skills needed to find things yourself or pushing your eyeball to the limit? Where's the intellectual challenge when you use a pre-programmed robot?' All these questions are absolutely valid – if your goal is to test your skill and endurance or to compete with your astronomical grandfather.

But let's look at the heart of this technological artichoke.

Many people have less free time than ever before, especially well-educated and affluent ones – precisely those who are most likely to adopt astronomy as a hobby. Since it takes time and patience to learn how to find things in the sky, many of these budding hobbyists can profit from a jump-start. Enter CATs! All you need do is dump one of these smart telescopes on the ground, locate a couple of bright stars to get its 'brain' thinking straight, and away you go! Even if you don't know what objects to look at, a built-in roster of tasty sights will start you off. Acquiring the skill to find things may be the greatest impediment to creating an observer. So why not launch a newcomer with a crutch that he or she can throw away at any time?

And, really, what *is* the difference between looking at a television screen and looking through an eyepiece? Sitting in your study, you will not feel the bite of the wind, or cold feet, or a probing mosquito. Is that bad? What is lost, of course, is experiencing your place under the vault of heaven or serendipitously witnessing a fireball or auroral burst.

At the edge of the envelope

Computer-as-observatory has enormous potential for dramatically and rapidly invading every corner of amateur astronomy. In fact, this concept is certain to impact our community in many ways that haven't yet been imagined. One frontier will be an expansion beyond hardware control and data reduction. Computer-as-observatory has the potential to flower into a multi-cultural, multi-interest *social experience*.

At the most basic level we should see many special-interest user groups form, connected by computer and telephone modem. Already the vast majority of professional astronomers routinely exchange information this way through world-wide networks. In the same spirit, amateurs widely use the Astroforum section of CompuServe as well as many electronic bulletin boards (some operated by clubs, others by individuals). In an ideal world, *everyone* would be connected – supernova hunters, timers of Jovian satellite eclipses, Astronomy Day organizers, light-pollution activists. There is tremendous opportunity here to significantly expand and integrate the world community of amateurs.

Such communication would allow bridges to be built between amateurs in developed and developing countries. Sophisticated telescopes and CCDs will remain beyond the reach of those in the Third World for many years. Yet electrons are readily and cheaply transported across international boundaries. How wonderful it would be to see world-wide sharing from the Western-style technological cornucopia! Imagine someone in Florida taking a CCD image of Mars and sending it to another amateur in India, one who can't afford high-tech detectors but who is a whiz at image processing and interpretation. Opportunities for such 'hands-across-the-nations' initiatives abound and seem to be just around the corner. Amateurs could begin to emulate the traditions of shortwave radio operators. Such a cross-cultural network would not only foster the exchange of technical information, it could also serve as an extremely powerful vehicle for education at all levels and in all societies.

I began to appreciate the concept of computer-as-observatory in the mid-1980s after attending a meeting of the International Amateur-Professional Photoelectric Photometry group. Russ Genet was one of the meeting's organizers, and he and his colleagues spoke about the latest developments for *robotic observatories*. That, of course, is the next logical step beyond robotic telescopes – the shelter is automated as well as the instrument itself. When sensors find the sky clear, the observatory roof opens and the telescope begins a pre-programmed cycle of observations – humans need not be present, except via computer and telephone link if they choose. When the night's work is over, the roof shuts, the telescope is stowed, and the data are either archived or sent to the observer.

Since an automatic observatory can operate anywhere, Genet soon expanded his vision to include observatories on Earth-orbiting satellites and even on the Moon! And Kitt Peak astronomer David Crawford began to envision a Global Network of Automatic Telescopes (GNAT), where each instrument acts as part of a unified system to keep objects under surveillance twenty-four hours a day.

Yet the brightest star in contemporary amateur astronomy is the CCD. So staggering is its potential that in not too many years these devices may well be offered as standard equipment on all top-notch commercial telescopes. CCDs will be part of the package, just as cellular phones are standard equipment on some luxury cars.

The CCDs presently available to amateurs are limited by their small size (less than a half inch across) and the number of picture elements they contain (typically 100,000). Nevertheless, they are perfectly adequate for imaging a wide variety of objects, from planets to galaxies. Their biggest drawback is that the field of view is

Figure 3. This CCD chip is less than a half inch across and is typical of those used by amateurs today. (Courtesy *Sky & Telescope*)

very small, making it difficult to find a target. On an 8-inch, f/10 telescope, the field of such an array is only 15 arc minutes across or half the diameter of the full Moon.

CCDs yielding wider fields will certainly become available. Yet the biggest gain between now and the end of this century should be a dramatic decrease in price. If CCD pricing roughly tracks that of computers over the last decade, a camera selling for $3000 today will sell for $500 by the year 2000.

As chips get larger and contain more picture elements, more computer power will be needed – lots more computer power. Here too the future looks bright. As Roger Sinnott reported in the May 1992 issue of *Sky & Telescope*, today's $3000 computer ran faster in one application than a Cray super-computer did five years ago. Data-storage will also be no problem thanks to rapidly advancing technology at affordable prices – CD-ROMs, optical disks, and computer hard disks with incredible capacity.

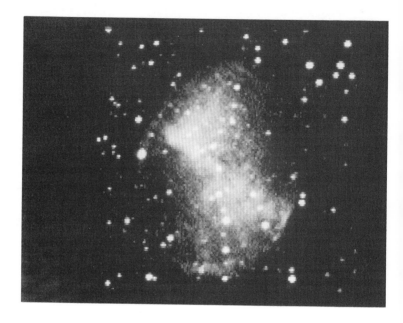

Figure 4. The power of the CCD becomes evident in this 1-minute exposure of the Dumb-bell nebula, M27. It was snatched from London's light-polluted skies with a 10-inch telescope. (Courtesy Maurice Gavin)

The applications of CCDs, now and soon-to-be, are truly staggering. The impact will not only affect amateur research by sophisticates; it will affect amateur astronomers who are out merely to have fun! CCDs may actually be the last hope for preserving the hobby among people who toil under increasingly light-polluted skies. Because of their ability to remove a bright-sky background, to enhance contrast, and to make short exposures through light-pollution filters, CCDs will open unimaginable vistas for amateurs trapped in a sea of artificial light.

Not only deep-sky objects yield to the CCD, planets do as well. Amateur astronomers can now record details perhaps ten times

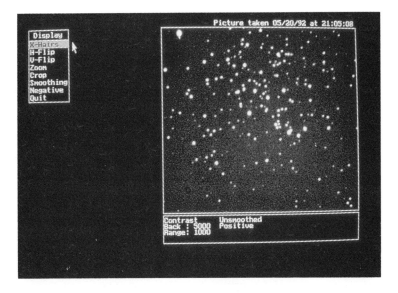

Figure 5. This 10-second CCD exposure with an 11-inch Schmidt-Cassegrain captured 15th-magnitude stars in M67 even though evening twilight was so bright that the open cluster was invisible in a 5-inch guidescope. (Courtesy Dennis di Cicco)

finer than they could with conventional photography. The rapid exposures possible with a CCD permit observers to enhance resolution greatly even under mediocre atmospheric conditions. This is not to say that CCDs improve poor seeing, but they do allow you to get the better of it if you're patient.

Because CCD images are digital, they can be readily manipulated through the technique of image processing, an enormous advance over traditional darkroom techniques. You can have your computer enhance or suppress whatever details you like, add artificial colour, create contours of equal intensity, measure positions and brightnesses, and so on. The computer software needed to accomplish all of this is readily available to amateurs though it was unimagined just a few years ago. And, surely, vastly improved versions will rapidly make their way into the market place. For example, one scheme will allow you to manipulate images of deep-sky objects to make them appear on your monitor as they would in the eyepiece of any size telescope you choose!

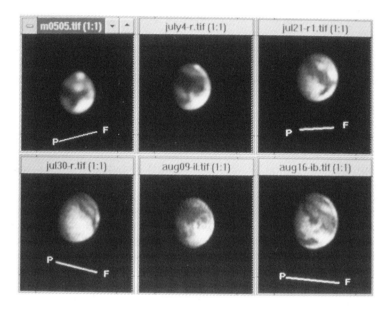

Figure 6. This remarkable sequence was made with a CCD and 16-inch Newtonian reflector. It shows Mars' disk growing in size from May to mid-August 1992 (in the last image, Mars is only 7 arcseconds across!). The amount of detail resolved on the planet's disk is truly amazing. (Courtesy Donald Parker)

Applications of CCDs are limited only by the imagination of the user, and here there needs to be a re-alignment of thinking about what amateurs can do.

For example, Dennis di Cicco now captures faint deep-sky objects in vivid 'true' colours. He 'merely' transferred the principles of three-colour photography to the CCD by carefully selecting a set of filters that match the CCD's light-response at selected wavelengths. His images, therefore, are free from the idiosyncrasies of photographic colour emulsions after they are exposed for tens of minutes.

There are also important research projects awaiting those who will seize the moment. For the foreseeable future amateurs will have increasing and unprecedented opportunities to make major discoveries. The strategy, of course, is to exploit niches in which professionals can't compete or in which they have lost interest. The competition issue is won, as it has traditionally been, by taking advantage of time and opportunity. Amateurs have the luxury of observing whenever they want, professionals do not. Exploring presumed dead-ends holds promise because there's no telling what fresh revelations the new technologies will spawn. There must be scores of unique projects awaiting the savvy amateur. I'll toss out three examples. And to emphasize my point, the first two will pertain to one of the 'deadest' disciplines in contemporary astronomy – double stars.

Take, for example, the suggestion by Harold McAlister that amateurs using CCDs can resolve extremely close double stars through the technique of speckle interferometry. (This process overcomes atmospheric turbulence and re-creates a nearly diffraction-limited image through a mathematical technique.) McAlister, who has done more speckle work on doubles than anyone else, believes that a 16-inch telescope equipped with an inexpensive CCD and frame-grabber should be able to approach the performance of a 40-inch refractor used conventionally! He points out that there are a couple of hundred doubles brighter than 7th magnitude that should yield to such a system. Imagine watching a binary star change its position month by month and complete a full orbit in only a decade or so! Amateur double-star observers once formed the backbone of this discipline. With modern technology and mentors like McAlister, they could well help re-vitalize this important and sadly neglected field.

That's pretty heady stuff! A less challenging but potentially equally rewarding project would be to monitor the components of double and multiple stars for variations in their light on both short (minutes to hours) and long (days to months) time scales. Almost nothing is known about the variability of the components of optical double stars. Discovering what kinds of variations are on-going would lead to a better understanding of the types of stars that comprise such systems and perhaps would say something about the star-forming process itself. We should recall that the westernmost component of the Orion nebula's Trapezium – the most looked-at patch of sky for more than three centuries – went unnoticed as a variable star until 1973! It's an eclipsing star with a range of one

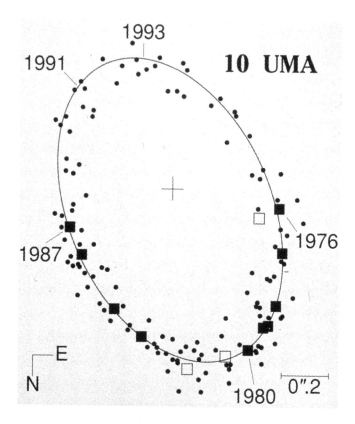

Figure 7. Harold McAlister's orbit of 10 Ursæ Majoris, a binary star that completes a revolution every two decades. Measurements made by the technique of speckle interferometry are plotted as squares to set them off from traditional observations. (Courtesy the author)

magnitude, so its variations are larger than BM Orionis (the northernmost Trapezium member), which itself was only discovered to eclipse in 1917.

Let's now jump from the familiar though unknown to the utterly unknown. For example, why shouldn't amateurs seek comets in the Kuiper Belt – a purported disk beyond Pluto where thousands of these objects spend their lives? Or why shouldn't amateurs find planets, if they exist, roaming freely throughout our Galaxy and perhaps being the putative dark material that makes up 90–99 per cent of the Universe? No matter that both kinds of objects are thousands or millions of times fainter than anything amateurs have ever recorded. Crazy suggestion? No, at least according to Freeman Dyson, one of the great thinkers of the twentieth century. His search strategy is simple – look for comets or planets as they intercept the light of stars! For Kuiper-Belt comets, he figures one of them would pass in front of (and dim) a star every two days as seen from a single place on Earth. For planets, the reverse is true – they would gravitationally lens the star's light and brighten it! Alas, the latter events are expected to be few and far between, perhaps one per year as monitored by a hundred telescopes looking at different star fields.

But who cares what the odds seem to be for detecting Kuiper-Belt comets or rogue planets – the predictions are only educated guesses. My point is this: amateurs should not shy away from testing new ideas or applying new technologies. Perhaps they could even up the ante, if they were given some help by professionals. Is the time right for forming an amateur–professional alliance (modelled on that of the International Amateur–Professional Photoelectric Photometry group) to look for challenging projects that *only* amateurs could complete in a cost-effective way? Some, like that suggested by Dyson, would be very high-risk – precisely the kind that 'establishment' scientists wouldn't be permitted to undertake. Others, like the ones on double stars, simply need professional guidance.

Many more exciting technological prospects lie in the future, but my crystal ball begins to mist over. How long will it be before amateurs gain access to infrared wavelengths and the opportunity to witness starbirth? How long before they have their own observatory in space? When will 'adaptive optics' routinely take the jiggle out of starlight and yield diffraction-limited performance to amateur telescopes? (Within a week of writing that sentence, Stellar Products of Colorado Springs, Colorado, announced the availability of just such a device! Is there any better demonstration of how fast our hobby is expanding technologically?)

Moving away from hardware, amateurs are gaining access to enormous databases – literally, the cores of major observatory libraries. For example, a CD-ROM released by NASA in 1991 contains 114 astronomical catalogues (Figure 8), including practically all the ones an amateur would ever want: the *SAO Star Catalog*, the *Washington Catalog of Double Stars*, the *Uppsala General Catalogue of Galaxies*, and many more. For about $30

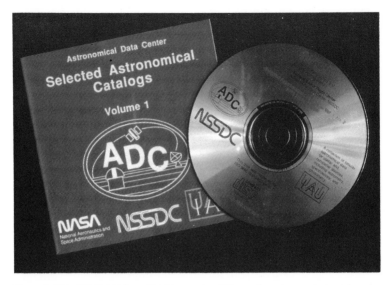

Figure 8. This CD-ROM from NASA contains 114 popular astronomical catalogues. (Courtesy *Sky & Telescope*)

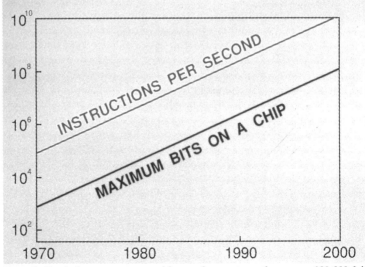

Figure 9. Here's the past, present, and future of computer performance – 100,000-fold gains in only three decades. (Courtesy the author)

(approx. £20) you get 680 megabytes of information. Amazing! There are now about 20 NASA CD-ROMs that cover topics from the International Halley Watch, to data from the Infrared Astronomical Satellite, to imagery from Magellan.

In the next few years we will see a deluge of CD-ROMs and optical disks that contain images. It would not be too wild a guess to predict that the entire NASA collection of space-craft images will become available sometime soon, as well as images from other space-based observatories. (In fact, you can already obtain images from the Hubble Space Telescope for processing on your personal computer.) And it is probably just a matter of time before ground-based observatories also begin to issue massive collections of archival pictures.

One of the most amazing resources ever released appeared in 1991. It is the Buil-Thouvenot *CCD Atlas of Deep-Sky Objects*, a collection of electronic images portraying more than 3000 galaxies, nebulæ, and clusters. Nothing approaching the thoroughness of this atlas has ever appeared in a conventional book.

Dreams or reality?

Why should anyone believe these speculations? Consider this. In the 1960s, Gordon Moore, a founder of the world-famous Intel Corporation that manufactures semiconductor chips for computers, stated that the capacity of the chips would double every two years. He now believes their capacity will double every year and a half. Presently, memory chips can store about four million bytes of information, so from Moore's law we can expect their capacity to approach 100 million bytes by the end of the century. Not surprisingly, in mid-1992 IBM, Siemens, and Toshiba announced they would jointly develop a chip with a capacity of 256 megabytes. That's ahead of Moore's law!

As a columnist for the *Boston Globe* put it: 'By the end of the decade, schoolchildren will be playing with video-game equipment . . . as powerful as today's supercomputers.' Is it any wonder I can't help but believe that such technological mega-advances will fill every nook and cranny of amateur astronomy? An enormously exciting future awaits even the most pedestrian consumer of starlight. That includes folks like me, who have to be shown where the on-off button is and which way to push it!

Some Interesting Variable Stars

JOHN ISLES

The following stars are of interest for many reasons. Of course, the periods and ranges of many variables are not constant from one cycle to another.

Star	R.A. h	m	Declination deg.	min.	Range	Type	Period days	Spectrum
R Andromedæ	00	24.0	+38	35	5.8–14.9	Mira	409	S
W Andromedæ	02	17.6	+44	18	6.7–14.6	Mira	396	S
U Antliæ	10	35.2	−39	34	5–6	Irregular	–	C
Theta Apodis	14	05.3	−76	48	5–7	Semi-regular	119	M
R Aquarii	23	43.8	−15	17	5.8–12.4	Symbiotic	387	M+Pec
T Aquarii	20	49.9	−05	09	7.2–14.2	Mira	202	M
R Aquilæ	19	06.4	+08	14	5.5–12.0	Mira	284	M
V Aquilæ	19	04.4	−05	41	6.6– 8.4	Semi-regular	353	C
Eta Aquilæ	19	52.5	+01	00	3.5– 4.4	Cepheid	7.2	F–G
U Aræ	17	53.6	−51	41	7.7–14.1	Mira	225	M
R Arietis	02	16.1	+25	03	7.4–13.7	Mira	187	M
U Arietis	03	11.0	+14	48	7.2–15.2	Mira	371	M
R Aurigæ	05	17.3	+53	35	6.7–13.9	Mira	458	M
Epsilon Aurigæ	05	02.0	+43	49	2.9– 3.8	Algol	9892	F+B
R Boötis	14	37.2	+26	44	6.2–13.1	Mira	223	M
W Boötis	14	43.4	+26	32	4.7– 5.4	Semi-regular?	450?	M
X Camelopardalis	04	45.7	+75	06	7.4–14.2	Mira	144	K–M
R Cancri	08	16.6	+11	44	6.1–11.8	Mira	362	M
X Cancri	08	55.4	+17	14	5.6– 7.5	Semi-regular	195?	C
R Canis Majoris	07	19.5	−16	24	5.7– 6.3	Algol	1.1	F
S Canis Minoris	07	32.7	+08	19	6.6–13.2	Mira	333	M
R Canum Ven.	13	49.0	+39	33	6.5–12.9	Mira	329	M
R Carinæ	09	32.2	−62	47	3.9–10.5	Mira	309	M
S Carinæ	10	09.4	−61	33	4.5– 9.9	Mira	149	K–M
l Carinæ	09	45.2	−62	30	3.3– 4.2	Cepheid	35.5	F–K
Eta Carinæ	10	45.1	−59	41	−0.8– 7.9	Irregular	–	Pec
R Cassiopeiæ	23	58.4	+51	24	4.7–13.5	Mira	430	M
S Cassiopeiæ	01	19.7	+72	37	7.9–16.1	Mira	612	S
W Cassiopeiæ	00	54.9	+58	34	7.8–12.5	Mira	406	C
Gamma Cass.	00	56.7	+60	43	1.6– 3.0	Irregular	–	B
Rho Cassiopeiæ	23	54.4	+57	30	4.1– 6.2	Semi-regular	–	F–K
R Centauri	14	16.6	−59	55	5.3–11.8	Mira	546	M
S Centauri	12	24.6	−49	26	7–8	Semi-regular	65	C
T Centauri	13	41.8	−33	36	5.5– 9.0	Semi-regular	90	K–M
S Cephei	21	35.2	+78	37	7.4–12.9	Mira	487	C
T Cephei	21	09.5	+68	29	5.2–11.3	Mira	388	M
Delta Cephei	22	29.2	+58	25	3.5– 4.4	Cepheid	5.4	F–G
Mu Cephei	21	43.5	+58	47	3.4– 5.1	Semi-regular	730	M
U Ceti	02	33.7	−13	09	6.8–13.4	Mira	235	M
W Ceti	00	02.1	−14	41	7.1–14.8	Mira	351	S
Omicron Ceti	02	19.3	−02	59	2.0–10.1	Mira	332	M

Star	R.A. h	m	Declination deg.	min.	Range	Type	Period days	Spectrum
R Chamæleontis	08	21.8	−76	21	7.5–14.2	Mira	335	M
T Columbæ	05	19.3	−33	42	6.6–12.7	Mira	226	M
R Comæ Ber.	12	04.3	+18	47	7.1–14.6	Mira	363	M
R Coronæ Bor.	15	48.6	+28	09	5.7–14.8	R Coronæ Bor.	–	C
S Coronæ Bor.	15	21.4	+31	22	5.8–14.1	Mira	360	M
T Coronæ Bor.	15	59.6	+25	55	2.0–10.8	Recurr. nova	–	M+Pec
V Coronæ Bor.	15	49.5	+39	34	6.9–12.6	Mira	358	C
W Coronæ Bor.	16	15.4	+37	48	7.8–14.3	Mira	238	M
R Corvi	12	19.6	−19	15	6.7–14.4	Mira	317	M
R Crucis	12	23.6	−61	38	6.4– 7.2	Cepheid	5.8	F–G
R Cygni	19	36.8	+50	12	6.1–14.4	Mira	426	S
U Cygni	20	19.6	+47	54	5.9–12.1	Mira	463	C
W Cygni	21	36.0	+45	22	5.0– 7.6	Semi-regular	131	M
RT Cygni	19	43.6	+48	47	6.0–13.1	Mira	190	M
SS Cygni	21	42.7	+43	35	7.7–12.4	Dwarf nova	50±	K+Pec
CH Cygni	19	24.5	+50	14	5.6– 9.0	Symbiotic	–	M+B
Chi Cygni	19	50.6	+32	55	3.3–14.2	Mira	408	S
R Delphini	20	14.9	+09	05	7.6–13.8	Mira	285	M
U Delphini	20	45.5	+18	05	5.6– 7.5	Semi-regular	110?	M
EU Delphini	20	37.9	+18	16	5.8– 6.9	Semi-regular	60	M
Beta Doradus	05	33.6	−62	29	3.5– 4.1	Cepheid	9.8	F–G
R Draconis	16	32.7	+66	45	6.7–13.2	Mira	246	M
T Eridani	03	55.2	−24	02	7.2–13.2	Mira	252	M
R Fornacis	02	29.3	−26	06	7.5–13.0	Mira	389	C
R Geminorum	07	07.4	+22	42	6.0–14.0	Mira	370	S
U Geminorum	07	55.1	+22	00	8.2–14.9	Dwarf nova	105±	Pec+M
Zeta Geminorum	07	04.1	+20	34	3.6– 4.2	Cepheid	10.2	F–G
Eta Geminorum	06	14.9	+22	30	3.2– 3.9	Semi-regular	233	M
S Gruis	22	26.1	−48	26	6.0–15.0	Mira	402	M
S Herculis	16	51.9	+14	56	6.4–13.8	Mira	307	M
U Herculis	16	25.8	+18	54	6.4–13.4	Mira	406	M
Alpha Herculis	17	14.6	+14	23	2.7– 4.0	Semi-regular	–	M
68, u Herculis	17	17.3	+33	06	4.7– 5.4	Algol	2.1	B+B
R Horologii	02	53.9	−49	53	4.7–14.3	Mira	408	M
U Horologii	03	52.8	−45	50	6–14	Mira	348	M
R Hydræ	13	29.7	−23	17	3.5–10.9	Mira	389	M
U Hydræ	10	37.6	−13	23	4.3– 6.5	Semi-regular	450?	C
VW Hydri	04	09.1	−71	18	8.4–14.4	Dwarf nova	27±	Pec
R Leonis	09	47.6	+11	26	4.4–11.3	Mira	310	M
R Leonis Minoris	09	45.6	+34	31	6.3–13.2	Mira	372	M
R Leporis	04	59.6	−14	48	5.5–11.7	Mira	427	C
Y Libræ	15	11.7	−06	01	7.6–14.7	Mira	276	M
RS Libræ	15	24.3	−22	55	7.0–13.0	Mira	218	M
Delta Libræ	15	01.0	−08	31	4.9– 5.9	Algol	2.3	A
R Lyncis	07	01.3	+55	20	7.2–14.3	Mira	379	S
R Lyræ	18	55.3	+43	57	3.9– 5.0	Semi-regular	46?	M
RR Lyræ	19	25.5	+42	47	7.1– 8.1	RR Lyræ	0.6	A–F
Beta Lyræ	18	50.1	+33	22	3.3– 4.4	Eclipsing	12.9	B
U Microscopii	20	29.2	−40	25	7.0–14.4	Mira	334	M
U Monocerotis	07	30.8	−09	47	5.9– 7.8	RV Tauri	91	F–K
V Monocerotis	06	22.7	−02	12	6.0–13.9	Mira	340	M
R Normæ	15	36.0	−49	30	6.5–13.9	Mira	508	M
T Normæ	15	44.1	−54	59	6.2–13.6	Mira	241	M
R Octantis	05	26.1	−86	23	6.3–13.2	Mira	405	M
S Octantis	18	08.7	−86	48	7.2–14.0	Mira	259	M
V Ophiuchi	16	26.7	−12	26	7.3–11.6	Mira	297	C
X Ophiuchi	18	38.3	+08	50	5.9– 9.2	Mira	329	M
RS Ophiuchi	17	50.2	−06	43	4.3–12.5	Recurr. nova	–	OB+M
U Orionis	05	55.8	+20	10	4.8–13.0	Mira	368	M
W Orionis	05	05.4	+01	11	5.9– 7.7	Semi-regular	212	C

217

Star	R.A.		Declination		Range	Type	Period	Spectrum
	h	m	deg.	min.			days	
Alpha Orionis	05	55.2	+07	24	0.0– 1.3	Semi-regular	2335	M
S Pavonis	19	55.2	−59	12	6.6–10.4	Semi-regular	381	M
Kappa Pavonis	18	56.9	−67	14	3.9– 4.8	Cepheid	9.1	G
R Pegasi	23	06.8	+10	33	6.9–13.8	Mira	378	M
Beta Pegasi	23	03.8	+28	05	2.3– 2.7	Irregular	–	M
X Persei	03	55.4	+31	03	6.0– 7.0	Gamma Cass.	–	O9.5
Beta Persei	03	08.2	+40	57	2.1– 3.4	Algol	2.9	B
Rho Persei	03	05.2	+38	50	3.3– 4.0	Semi-regular	50?	M
Zeta Phœnicis	01	08.4	−55	15	3.9– 4.4	Algol	1.7	B+B
R Pictoris	04	46.2	−49	15	6.4–10.1	Semi-regular	171	M
L² Puppis	07	13.5	−44	39	2.6– 6.2	Semi-regular	141	M
T Pyxidis	09	04.7	−32	23	6.5–15.3	Recurr. nova	7000±	Pec
U Sagittæ	19	18.8	+19	37	6.5– 9.3	Algol	3.4	B+G
WZ Sagittæ	20	07.6	+17	42	7.0–15.5	Dwarf nova	11900±	A
R Sagittarii	19	16.7	−19	18	6.7–12.8	Mira	270	M
RR Sagittarii	19	55.9	−29	11	5.4–14.0	Mira	336	M
RT Sagittarii	20	17.7	−39	07	6.0–14.1	Mira	306	M
RU Sagittarii	19	58.7	−41	51	6.0–13.8	Mira	240	M
RY Sagittarii	19	16.5	−33	31	5.8–14.0	R Coronæ Bor.	–	G
RR Scorpii	16	56.6	−30	35	5.0–12.4	Mira	281	M
RS Scorpii	16	55.6	−45	06	6.2–13.0	Mira	320	M
RT Scorpii	17	03.5	−36	55	7.0–15.2	Mira	449	S
S Sculptoris	00	15.4	−32	03	5.5–13.6	Mira	363	M
R Scuti	18	47.5	−05	42	4.2– 8.6	RV Tauri	146	G–K
R Serpentis	15	50.7	+15	08	5.2–14.4	Mira	356	M
S Serpentis	15	21.7	+14	19	7.0–14.1	Mira	372	M
T Tauri	04	22.0	+19	32	9.3–13.5	Irregular	–	F–K
SU Tauri	05	49.1	+19	04	9.1–16.9	R Coronæ Bor.	–	G
Lambda Tauri	04	00.7	+12	29	3.4– 3.9	Algol	4.0	B+A
R Trianguli	02	37.0	+34	16	5.4–12.6	Mira	267	M
R Ursæ Majoris	10	44.6	+68	47	6.5–13.7	Mira	302	M
T Ursæ Majoris	12	36.4	+59	29	6.6–13.5	Mira	257	M
U Ursæ Minoris	14	17.3	+66	48	7.1–13.0	Mira	331	M
R Virginis	12	38.5	+06	59	6.1–12.1	Mira	146	M
S Virginis	13	33.0	−07	12	6.3–13.2	Mira	375	M
SS Virginis	12	25.3	+00	48	6.0– 9.6	Semi-regular	364	C
R Vulpeculæ	21	04.4	+23	49	7.0–14.3	Mira	137	M
Z Vulpeculæ	19	21.7	+25	34	7.3– 8.9	Algol	2.5	B+A

Mira Stars: maxima, 1994

JOHN ISLES

Below are given predicted dates of maxima for Mira stars that reach magnitude 7.5 or brighter at an average maximum. Individual maxima can in some cases be brighter or fainter than average by a magnitude or more, and all dates are only approximate. The positions, extreme ranges and mean periods of these stars can all be found in the preceding list of interesting variable stars.

Star	Mean magnitude at maximum	Dates of maxima
W Andromedæ	7.4	Apr. 1
R Aquarii	6.5	Feb. 7
R Aquilæ	6.1	Jan. 18, Oct. 30
R Boötis	7.2	Mar. 22, Oct. 31
R Cancri	6.8	Oct. 30
S Canis Minoris	7.5	June 30
R Carinæ	4.6	Jan. 18, Nov. 23
S Carinæ	5.7	Apr. 8, Sep. 5
R Cassiopeiæ	7.0	Nov. 3
R Centauri	5.8	June 21
T Cephei	6.0	Dec. 29
U Ceti	7.5	Mar. 5, Oct. 25
Omicron Ceti	3.4	May 16
T Columbæ	7.5	Feb. 12, Sep. 26
S Coronæ Borealis	7.3	Oct. 11
V Coronæ Borealis	7.5	May 11
R Corvi	7.5	Mar. 23
U Cygni	7.2	Oct. 4
RT Cygni	7.3	June 21, Dec. 28
Chi Cygni	5.2	May 31
R Geminorum	7.1	Oct. 21
U Herculis	7.5	Apr. 28
R Horologii	6.0	July 4
U Horologii	7	Mar. 1
R Hydræ	4.5	Jan. 30
R Leonis	5.8	May 12
R Leonis Minoris	7.1	Aug. 7
R Leporis	6.8	Apr. 27
RS Libræ	7.5	July 26
V Monocerotis	7.0	Oct. 26
T Normæ	7.4	Apr. 26, Dec. 23

Star	Mean magnitude at maximum	Dates of maxima
V Ophiuchi	7.5	July 24
X Ophiuchi	6.8	Feb. 6
U Orionis	6.3	Nov. 17
R Sagittarii	7.3	June 29
RR Sagittarii	6.8	May 3
RT Sagittarii	7.0	Mar. 30
RU Sagittarii	7.2	Jan. 7, Sep. 4
RR Scorpii	5.9	Sep. 22
RS Scorpii	7.0	Apr. 15
S Sculptoris	6.7	Nov. 29
R Serpentis	6.9	Mar. 25
R Trianguli	6.2	May 28
R Ursæ Majoris	7.5	May 24
R Virginis	6.9	Jan. 14, June 9, Nov. 1
S Virginis	7.0	Aug. 29

Some Interesting Double Stars

R. W. ARGYLE

The positions given below correspond to epoch 1995.0

Name	Magnitudes	Separation in seconds of arc	Position angle, degrees	Notes
Gamma Andromedæ	2.3, 5.0	9.4	064	Yellow, blue. B is again double.
Zeta Aquarii	4.3, 4.5	2.0	196	Slowly widening.
Gamma Arietis	4.8, 4.8	7.6	000	Very easy. Both white.
Epsilon Arietis	5.2, 5.5	1.5	208	Binary. Both white.
Theta Aurigæ	2.6, 7.1	3.7	310	Stiff test for 3-in.
44 Boötis	5.3, 6.2	2.0	051	Period 246 years.
xi Boötis	4.7, 7.0	6.9	322	Fine contrast. Easy.
Epsilon Boötis	2.5, 4.9	2.8	342	Yellow, blue. Fine pair.
Zeta Cancri	5.6, 6.2	6.0	074	A again double.
Iota Cancri	4.2, 6.6	30.4	307	Easy. Yellow, blue.
Alpha Canum Ven.	2.9, 5.5	19.6	228	Easy. Yellow, bluish.
Upsilon Carinæ	3.1, 6.1	5.0	127	Fixed.
Eta Cassiopeiæ	3.4, 7.5	12.7	315	Easy. Creamy, bluish.
Alpha Centauri	0.0, 1.2	17.3	218	Very easy. Period 80 years.
Gamma Centauri	2.9, 2.9	1.2	351	Period 84 years. Closing. Both yellow.
3 Centauri	4.5, 6.0	7.8	105	Both white.
Beta Cephei	3.2, 7.9	14	250	Easy with a 3-in.
Delta Cephei	var, 7.5	41	192	Very easy.
Xi Cephei	4.4, 6.5	8.0	276	White, blue.
Gamma Ceti	3.5, 7.3	2.9	294	Not too easy.
Alpha Circini	3.2, 8.6	15.7	230	PA slowly decreasing.
Zeta Corona Bor.	5.1, 6.0	6.3	305	PA slowly increasing.
Delta Corvi	3.0, 9.2	24	214	Easy with a 3-in.
Alpha Crucis	1.4, 1.9	4.2	114	Third star in a low-power field.
Gamma Crucis	1.6, 6.7	124	024	Third star in a low-power field.
Mu Crucis	4.3, 5.3	34.9	017	Fixed. Both white.
Beta Cygni	3.1, 5.1	34.1	054	Glorious. Yellow, blue.
61 Cygni	5.2, 6.0	30.2	149	Nearby binary. Period 722 years.
Gamma Delphini	4.5, 5.5	9.3	267	Easy. Yellowish, greenish.
Epsilon Draconis	3.8, 7.4	3.2	019	Slow binary.
Nu Draconis	4.9, 4.9	62	312	Naked eye pair.
f Eridani	4.8, 5.3	8.2	215	Pale yellow.
p Eridani	5.8, 5.8	11.4	192	Period 483 years.
Theta Eridani	3.4, 4.5	8.3	090	Both white.

Name	Magnitudes	Separation in seconds of arc	Position angle, degrees	Notes
Alpha Geminorum	1.9, 2.9	3.5	072	Widening. Easy with a 3-in.
Delta Geminorum	3.5, 8.2	5.9	224	Not too easy.
Alpha Herculis	var, 5.4	4.6	106	Red, green. Binary.
Delta Herculis	3.1, 8.2	10.4	276	Optical pair. Distance increasing.
Zeta Herculis	2.9, 5.5	1.4	061	Fine, rapid binary. Period 34 years.
Epsilon Hydræ	3.3, 6.8	2.7	298	PA slowly increasing.
Theta Indi	4.5, 7.0	6.7	266	Fine contrast.
Gamma Leonis	2.2, 3.5	4.4	125	Binary, 619 years.
Pi Lupi	4.6, 4.7	1.7	065	Widening.
Alpha Lyræ	0.0, 9.5	76	182	Optical pair. B is faint.
Epsilon[1] Lyr	5.0, 6.1	2.6	352	Quadruple system. Both
Epsilon[2] Lyr	5.2, 5.5	2.3	085	pairs visible in a 3-in.
Zeta Lyræ	4.3, 5.9	44	149	Fixed. Easy double.
Beta Muscæ	3.7, 4.0	1.3	039	Both white.
70 Ophiuchi	4.2, 6.0	2.5	168	Rapid motion.
Beta Orionis	0.1, 6.8	9.5	202	Can be seen with 3-in.
Iota Orionis	2.8, 6.9	11.8	141	Enmeshed in nebulosity.
Theta Orionis	6.7, 7.9	8.7	032	Trapezium in M42.
	5.1, 6.7	13.4	061	
Sigma Orionis	4.0, 10.3	11.4	238	Quintuple. A is a
	6.5, 7.5	30.1	231	close double.
Zeta Orionis	1.9, 4.0	2.4	162	Can be split in 3-in.
Xi Pavonis	4.4, 8.6	3.3	155	Orange and white.
Eta Persei	3.8, 8.5	28.5	300	Yellow, bluish.
Beta Phœnicis	4.0, 4.2	1.5	324	Slowly widening.
Beta Piscis Aust.	4.4, 7.9	30.4	172	Optical pair. Fixed.
Alpha Piscium	4.2, 5.1	1.9	275	Binary, 933 years.
Kappa Puppis	4.5, 4.7	9.8	318	Both white.
Alpha Scorpii	1.2, 5.4	2.7	274	Red, green.
Nu Scorpii	4.3, 6.4	42	336	Both again double.
Theta Serpentis	4.5, 5.4	22.3	103	Fixed. Very easy.
Alpha Tauri	0.9, 11.1	131	032	Wide, but B very faint in small telescopes.
Iota Trianguli	5.3, 6.9	3.9	070	Slow binary.
Beta Tucanæ	4.4, 4.8	27.1	170	Both again double.
Delta Tucanæ	4.5, 9.0	6.9	282	White, reddish.
Zeta Ursæ Majoris	2.3, 4.0	14.4	151	Very easy. Naked eye pair with Alcor.
Xi Ursæ Majoris	4.3, 4.8	1.1	317	Binary, 60 years. Opening. Needs a 4-in.
Delta Velorum	2.1, 5.1	2.0	140	Slowly closing.
s Velorum	6.2, 6.5	13.5	218	Fixed.
Gamma Virginis	3.5, 3.5	2.2	277	Binary, 168 years. Closing.
Theta Virginis	4.4, 9.4	7.1	343	Not too easy.
Gamma Volantis	3.9, 5.8	13.8	299	Very slow binary.

Some Interesting Nebulæ and Clusters

Object	R.A.		Dec.		Remarks
	h	*m*			
M.31 Andromedæ	00	40.7	+41	05	Great Galaxy, visible to naked eye.
H.VIII 78 Cassiopeiæ	00	41.3	+61	36	Fine cluster, between Gamma and Kappa Cassiopeiæ.
M.33 Trianguli	01	31.8	+30	28	Spiral. Difficult with small apertures.
H.VI 33–4 Persei	02	18.3	+56	59	Double cluster; Sword-handle.
△ 142 Doradûs	05	39.1	−69	09	Looped nebula round 30 Doradûs. Naked-eye. In Large Cloud of Magellan.
M.1 Tauri	05	32.3	+22	00	Crab Nebula, near Zeta Tauri.
M.42 Orionis	05	33.4	−05	24	Great Nebula. Contains the famous Trapezium, Theta Orionis.
M.35 Geminorum	06	06.5	+24	21	Open cluster near Eta Geminorum.
H.VII 2 Monocerotis	06	30.7	+04	53	Open cluster, just visible to naked eye.
M.41 Canis Majoris	06	45.5	−20	42	Open cluster, just visible to naked eye.
M.47 Puppis	07	34.3	−14	22	Mag. 5,2. Loose cluster.
H.IV 64 Puppis	07	39.6	−18	05	Bright planetary in rich neighbourhood.
M.46 Puppis	07	39.5	−14	42	Open cluster.
M.44 Cancri	08	38	+20	07	Præsepe. Open cluster near Delta Cancri. Visible to naked eye.
M.97 Ursæ Majoris	11	12.6	+55	13	Owl Nebula, diameter 3'. Planetary.
Kappa Crucis	12	50.7	−60	05	'Jewel Box'; open cluster, with stars of contrasting colours.
M.3 Can. Ven.	13	40.6	+28	34	Bright globular.
Omega Centauri	13	23.7	−47	03	Finest of all globulars. Easy with naked eye.
M.80 Scorpii	16	14.9	−22	53	Globular, between Antares and Beta Scorpionis.
M.4 Scorpii	16	21.5	−26	26	Open cluster close to Antares.
M.13 Herculis	16	40	+36	31	Globular. Just visible to naked eye.
M.92 Herculis	16	16.1	+43	11	Globular. Between Iota and Eta Herculis.
M.6 Scorpii	17	36.8	−32	11	Open cluster; naked eye.
M.7 Scorpii	17	50.6	−34	48	Very bright open cluster; naked eye.
M.23 Sagittarii	17	54.8	−19	01	Open cluster nearly 50' in diameter.
H.IV 37 Draconis	17	58.6	+66	38	Bright planetary.
M.8 Sagittarii	18	01.4	−24	23	Lagoon Nebula. Gaseous. Just visible with naked eye.
NGC 6572 Ophiuchi	18	10.9	+06	50	Bright planetary, between Beta Ophiuchi and Zeta Aquilæ.
M.17 Sagittarii	18	18.8	−16	12	Omega Nebula. Gaseous. Large and bright.
M.11 Scuti	18	49.0	−06	19	Wild Duck. Bright open cluster.
M.57 Lyræ	18	52.6	+32	59	Ring Nebula. Brightest of planetaries.
M.27 Vulpeculæ	19	58.1	+22	37	Dumb-bell Nebula, near Gamma Sagittæ.
H.IV 1 Aquarii	21	02.1	−11	31	Bright planetary near Nu Aquarii.
M.15 Pegasi	21	28.3	+12	01	Bright globular, near Epsilon Pegasi.
M.39 Cygni	21	31.0	+48	17	Open cluster between Deneb and Alpha Lacertæ. Well seen with low powers.

Our Contributors

David Jewitt was born in Tottenham, became interested in astronomy at the age of seven, and 'has never been able to shake it off'. He went to University College London, then to the California Institute of Technology for his Ph.D., and has been Professor of Astronomy at both MIT and the University of Hawaii, his present location. His main interest is in the Solar System, particularly comets.

David Allen continues his researches at the Anglo-Australian Observatory, where he has been for many years. He needs no introduction to our readers; the *Yearbook* would be incomplete without his contribution!

Peter Cattermole is a geologist by profession, and has been for years at the University of Sheffield. He is a Principal Scientific Investigator for NASA on the subject of Martian vulcanism. He is the author of several standard books, including *Planetary Volcanism* and *Mars*.

Ian McLean is one of the world's leading authorities in the field of infrared astronomy. He is Professor of Astronomy at UCLA, and Director of the Infra-Red Laboratory.

Allan Chapman, of Wadham College, Oxford, is a leading authority on astronomical history, and has published many research papers. He is a frequent and welcome contributor to the *Yearbook*.

Donald F. Trombino, of the Davis Memorial Solar Observatory in Florida, has been studying the Sun for many years, and has made many important contributions to solar research.

Leif Robinson has for many years been Editor of America's leading astronomical magazine, *Sky and Telescope*. He is also well known for his lecturing and his writing, and has played a very major role in the dissemination of astronomical knowledge.

The William Herschel Society maintains the museum now established at 19 New King Street, Bath – the only surviving Herschel House. It also undertakes activities of various kinds. New members would be welcome; those interested are asked to contact Dr L. Hilliard at 2 Lambridge, London Road, Bath.

Astronomical Societies in Great Britain

British Astronomical Association
Assistant Secretary: Burlington House, Piccadilly, London W1V 9AG.
Meetings: Lecture Hall of Scientific Societies, Civil Service Commission Building, 23 Savile Row, London W1. Last Wednesday each month (Oct.–June). 1700 hrs and some Saturday afternoons.

Association for Astronomy Education
Secretary: Bob Kibble, 34 Ackland Crescent, Denmark Hill, London SE5 8EQ.

Astronomy Ireland
Secretary: Antoinette Moore, PO Box 2888, Dublin 1.
Meetings: Ely House, 8 Ely Place, Dublin 2. 8 p.m., 2nd and 4th Mondays of each month September–April.

Astronomical Society of Wales
Secretary: John Minopoli, 12 Gwendoline Street, Port Talbot, West Glamorgan.

Federation of Astronomical Societies
Secretary: Mrs Christine Sheldon, Whitehaven, Lower Moor, Pershore, Worcs.

Junior Astronomical Society
Secretary: Guy Fennimore, 36 Fairway, Keyworth, Nottingham.
Meetings: London. Last Saturday Jan., April, July, Oct. 2.30 p.m. Details from Secretary.

Junior Astronomical Society of Ireland
Secretary: K. Nolan, 5 St Patrick's Crescent, Rathcoole, Co. Dublin.
Meetings: The Royal Dublin Society, Ballsbridge, Dublin 4. Monthly.

Aberdeen and District Astronomical Society
Secretary: Stephen Graham, 25 Davidson Place, Northfield, Aberdeen.
Meetings: Robert Gordon's Institute of Technology, St Andrew's Street, Aberdeen. Friday 7.30 p.m.

Altrincham and District Astronomical Society
Secretary: Colin Henshaw, 10 Delamore Road, Gatley, Cheadle, Cheshire.
Meetings: Public Library, Timperley. 1st Friday of each month, 7.30 p.m.

Astra Astronomy Section
Secretary: Ian Downie, 151 Sword Street, Glasgow G31.
Meetings: Public Library, Airdrie. Weekly.

Aylesbury Astronomical Society
Secretary: Nigel Sheridan, 22 Moor Park, Wendover, Bucks.
Meetings: 1st Monday in month. Details from Secretary.

Bassetlaw Astronomical Society
Secretary: P. R. Stanley, 39 Essex Road, Bircotes, nr. Doncaster.
Meetings: Rockware Glass, Sports & Social Club, Sandy Lane, Worksop, Notts. Tuesday fortnightly, 7.30 p.m.

Batley & Spenborough Astronomical Society
Secretary: Robert Morton, 22 Links Avenue, Cleckheaton, West Yorks BD19 4EG.
Meetings: Milner K. Ford Observatory, Wilton Park, Batley. Every Thursday, 7.30 p.m.

Bedford Astronomical Society
Secretary: D. Eagle, 24 Copthorne Close, Oakley, Bedford.
Meetings: Bedford School, Burnaby Rd, Bedford. Last Tuesday each month.

Bingham & Brookes Space Organization
Secretary: N. Bingham, 15 Hickmore's Lane, Lindfield, W. Sussex.

Birmingham Astronomical Society
Secretary: J. Spittles, 28 Milverton Road, Knowle, Solihull, West Midlands.
Meetings: Room 146, Aston University, last Tuesday each month, Sept. to June (except December moved to 1st week in January).

Blackpool & District Astronomical Society
Secretary: J. L. Crossley, 24 Fernleigh Close, Bispham, Blackpool, Lancs.

Bolton Astronomical Society
Secretary: Peter Miskiw, 9 Hedley Street, Bolton.

Border Astronomical Society
Secretary: David Pettit, 14 Shap Grove, Carlisle, Cumbria.

Boston Astronomers
Secretary: B. Tongue, South View, Fen Road, Stickford, Boston.
Meetings: Details from the Secretary.

Bradford Astronomical Society
Secretary: John Schofield, Briar Lea, Bromley Road, Bingley, W. Yorks.
Meetings: Eccleshill Library, Bradford 2. Monday fortnightly (with occasional variations).

Braintree, Halstead & District Astronomical Society
Secretary: Heather Reeder, The Knoll, St Peters in the Field, Braintree, Essex.
Meetings: St Peter's Church Hall, St Peter's Road, Braintree, Essex. 3rd Thursday each month, 8 p.m.

Bridgend Amateur Astronomical Society
Secretary: J. M. Pugsley, 32 Hoel Fawr, Broadlands, North Cornelly, Bridgend.
Meetings: G.P. Room, Recreation Centre, Bridgend, 1st and 3rd Friday monthly, 7.30 p.m.

Bridgwater Astronomical Society
Secretary: W. L. Buckland, 104 Polden Street, Bridgwater, Somerset.
Meetings: Room D10, Bridgwater College, Bath Road Centre, Bridgwater. 2nd Wednesday each month, Sept.–June.

Brighton Astronomical Society
Secretary: Mrs B. C. Smith, Flat 2, 23 Albany Villas, Hove, Sussex BN3 2RS.
Meetings: Preston Tennis Club, Preston Drive, Brighton. Weekly, Tuesdays.

Bristol Astronomical Society
Secretary: Y. A. Sage, 33 Mackie Avenue, Filton, Bristol.
Meetings: Royal Fort (Rm G44), Bristol University. Every Friday each month, Sept.–May. Fortnightly, June–August.

Cambridge Astronomical Association
Secretary: R. J. Greening, 20 Cotts Croft, Great Chishill, Royston, Herts.
Meetings: Venues as published in newsletter. 1st and 3rd Friday each month, 8 p.m.

Cardiff Astronomical Society
Secretary: D. W. S. Powell, 1 Tal-y-Bont Road, Ely, Cardiff.
Meeting Place: Room 230, Dept. Law, University College, Museum Avenue, Cardiff. Alternate Thursdays, 8 p.m.

Castle Point Astronomy Club
Secretary: Miss Zena White, 43 Lambeth Road, Eastwood, Essex.
Meetings: St Michael's Church, Thundersley. Most Wednesdays, 8 p.m.

Chelmsford Astronomers
Secretary: Brendan Clark, 5 Borda Close, Chelmsford, Essex.
Meetings: Once a month.

Chelmsford and District Astronomical Society
Secretary: Miss C. C. Puddick, 6 Walpole Walk, Rayleigh, Essex.
Meetings: Sandon House School, Sandon, near Chelmsford. 2nd and last Monday of month. 7.45 p.m.

Chester Astronomical Society
Secretary: Mrs S. Brooks, 39 Halton Road, Great Sutton, South Wirral.
Meetings: Southview Community Centre, Southview Road, Chester. Last Monday each month except Aug. and Dec., 7.30 p.m.

Chester Society of Natural Science Literature and Art
Secretary: Paul Braid, 'White Wing', 38 Bryn Avenue, Old Colwyn, Colwyn Bay, Clwyd.
Meetings: Grosvenor Museum, Chester. Fortnightly.

Chesterfield Astronomical Society
Secretary: P. Lisewski, 148 Old Hall Road, Brampton, Chesterfield.
Meetings: Barnet Observatory, Newbold. Each Friday.

Clacton & District Astronomical Society
Secretary: C. L. Haskell, 105 London Road, Clacton-on-Sea, Essex.

Cleethorpes & District Astronomical Society
Secretary: C. Illingworth, 38 Shaw Drive, Grimsby, S. Humberside.
Meetings: Beacon Hill Observatory, Cleethorpes. 1st Wednesday each month.

Cleveland & Darlington Astronomical Society
Secretary: Neil Haggath, 5 Fountains Crescent, Eston, Middlesbrough, Cleveland.
Meetings: Elmwood Community Centre, Greens Lane, Hartburn, Stockton-on-Tees. Monthly, usually second Friday.

Colchester Amateur Astronomers
Secretary: F. Kelly, 'Middleton', Church Road, Elmstead Market, Colchester, Essex.
Meetings: William Loveless Hall, High Street, Wivenhoe. Friday evenings. Fortnightly.

Cotswold Astronomical Society
Secretary: Trevor Talbot, Innisfree, Winchcombe Road, Sedgebarrow, Worcs.
Meetings: Fortnightly in Cheltenham or Gloucester.

Coventry & Warwicks Astronomical Society
Secretary: V. Cooper, 5 Gisburn Close, Woodloes Park, Warwick.
Meetings: Coventry Technical College. 1st Friday each month, Sept.–June.

Crawley Astronomical Society
Secretary: G. Cowley, 67 Climpixy Road, Ifield, Crawley, Sussex.
Meetings: Crawley College of Further Education. Monthly Oct.–June.

Crayford Manor House Astronomical Society
Secretary: R. H. Chambers, Manor House Centre, Crayford, Kent.
Meetings: Manor House Centre, Crayford. Monthly during term-time.

Croydon Astronomical Society
Secretary: N. Fisher, 5 Dagmar Road, London SE25 6HZ.
Meetings: Lanfranc High School, Mitcham Road, Croydon. Alternate Fridays, 7.45 p.m.
Derby & District Astronomical Society
Secretary: Jane D. Kirk, 7 Cromwell Avenue, Findern, Derby.
Meetings: At home of Secretary. First and third Friday each month, 7.30 p.m.
Doncaster Astronomical Society
Secretary: J. A. Day, 297 Lonsdale Avenue, Intake, Doncaster.
Meetings: Fridays, weekly.
Dundee Astronomical Society
Secretary: G. Young, 37 Polepark Road, Dundee, Angus.
Meetings: Mills Observatory, Balgay Park, Dundee. First Friday each month, 7.30 p.m. Sept.–
April.
Easington and District Astronomical Society
Secretary: T. Bradley, 52 Jameson Road, Hartlepool, Co. Durham.
Meetings: Easington Comprehensive School, Easington Colliery. Every third Thursday throughout
the year, 7.30 p.m.
Eastbourne Astronomical Society
Secretary: D. C. Gates, Apple Tree Cottage, Stunts Green, Hertsmonceux, East Sussex.
Meetings: St Aiden's Church Hall, 1 Whitley Road, Eastbourne. Monthly (except July and August).
East Lancashire Astronomical Society
Secretary: D. Chadwick, 16 Worston Lane, Great Harwood, Blackburn BB6 7TH.
Meetings: As arranged. Monthly.
Astronomical Society of Edinburgh
Secretary: R. G. Fenoulhet, 7 Greenend Gardens, Edinburgh EH17 7QB.
Meetings: City Observatory, Calton Hill, Edinburgh. Monthly.
Edinburgh University Astronomical Society
Secretary: c/o Dept. of Astronomy, Royal Observatory, Blackford Hill, Edinburgh.
Ewell Astronomical Society
Secretary: Edward Hanna, 91 Tennyson Avenue, Motspur Park, Surrey.
Meetings: 1st Friday of each month.
Exeter Astronomical Society
Secretary: Miss J. Corey, 5 Egham Avenue, Topsham Road, Exeter.
Meetings: The Meeting Room, Wynards, Magdalen Street, Exeter. 1st Thursday of month.
Farnham Astronomical Society
Secretary: Laurence Anslow, 14 Wellington Lane, Farnham, Surrey.
Meetings: Church House, Union Road, Farnham. 2nd Monday each month, 7.45 p.m.
Fitzharry's Astronomical Society (Oxford & District)
Secretary: Mark Harman, 20 Lapwing Lane, Cholsey, Oxon.
Meetings: All Saints Methodist Church, Dorchester Crescent, Abingdon, Oxon.
Furness Astronomical Society
Secretary: A. Thompson, 52 Ocean Road, Walney Island, Barrow-in-Furness, Cumbria.
Meetings: St Mary's Church Centre, Dalton-in-Furness. 2nd Saturday in month, 7.30 p.m. No August
meeting.
Fylde Astronomical Society
Secretary: 28 Belvedere Road, Thornton, Lancs.
Meetings: Stanley Hall, Rossendale Avenue South. 1st Wednesday each month.
Astronomical Society of Glasgow
Secretary: Malcolm Kennedy, 32 Cedar Road, Cumbernauld, Glasgow.
Meetings: University of Strathclyde, George St., Glasgow. 3rd Thursday each month, Sept.–April.
Greenock Astronomical Association
Secretary: Miss Fiona McKechnie, 19 Grey Place, Greenock.
Meetings: Greenock Arts Guild, 3 Campbell Street, Greenock.
Grimsby Astronomical Society
Secretary: R. Williams, 14 Richmond Close, Grimsby, South Humberside.
Meetings: Secretary's home. 2nd Thursday each month, 7.30 p.m.
Guernsey: La Société Guernesiaise Astronomy Section
Secretary: G. Falla, Highcliffe, Avenue Beauvais, Ville du Roi, St Peter's Port, Guernsey.
Meetings: The Observatory, St Peter's, Tuesdays, 8 p.m.
Guildford Association Society
Secretary: Mrs Joan Prosser, 115 Farnham Road, Guildford, Surrey.
Meetings: Guildford Institute, Ward Street, Guildford. 1st Thursday each month. Sept.–June,
7.30 p.m.
Gwynedd Astronomical Society
Secretary: P. J. Curtis, Ael-y-bryn, Malltraeth St Newborough, Anglesey, Gwynedd.
Meetings: Physics Lecture Room, Bangor University. 1st Thursday each month, 7.30 p.m.
The Hampshire Astronomical Group
Secretary: R. F. Dodd, 1 Conifer Close, Cowplain, Waterlooville, Hants.
Meetings: Clanfield Observatory. Each Friday, 7.30 p.m.

Astronomical Society of Haringey
  Secretary: Wally Baker, 58 Stirling Road, Wood Green, London N22.
  Meetings: The Hall of the Good Shepherd, Berwick Road, Wood Green. 3rd Wednesday each month, 8 p.m.
Harrogate Astronomical Society
  Secretary: P. Barton, 31 Gordon Avenue, Harrogate, North Yorkshire.
  Meetings: Harlow Hill Methodist Church Hall, 121 Otley Road, Harrogate. Last Friday each month.
Heart of England Astronomical Society
  Secretary: Jean Poyner, 67 Ellerton Road, Kingstanding, Birmingham B44 0QE.
  Meetings: Furnace End Village, every Thursday.
Hebden Bridge Literary & Scientific Society, Astronomical Section
  Secretary: F. Parker, 48 Caldene Avenue, Mytholmroyd, Hebden Bridge, West Yorkshire.
Herschel Astronomy Society
  Secretary: D. R. Whittaker, 149 Farnham Lane, Slough.
  Meetings: Eton College, 2nd Friday each month.
Howards Astronomy Club
  Secretary: H. Ilett, 22 St Georges Avenue, Warblington, Havant, Hants.
  Meetings: To be notified.
Huddersfield Astronomical and Philosophical Society
  Secretary (Assistant): M. Armitage, 37 Frederick Street, Crossland Moor, Huddersfield.
  Meetings: 4A Railway Street, Huddersfield. Every Friday, 7.30 p.m.
Hull and East Riding Astronomical Society
  Secretary: J. I. Booth, 3 Lynngarth Avenue, Cottingham, North Humberside.
  Meetings: Ferens Recreation Centre, Chanterlands Avenue, Hull. 1st Friday each month, Oct.–April, 7.30 p.m.
Ilkeston & District Astronomical Society
  Secretary: Trevor Smith, 129 Heanor Road, Smalley, Derbyshire.
  Meetings: The Friends Meeting Room, Ilkeston Museum, Ilkeston. 2nd Tuesday monthly, 7.30 p.m.
Ipswich, Orwell Astronomical Society
  Secretary: R. Gooding, 168 Ashcroft Road, Ipswich.
  Meetings: Orwell Park Observatory, Nacton, Ipswich. Wednesdays 8 p.m.
Irish Astronomical Association
  Secretary: Michael Duffy, 26 Ballymurphy Road, Belfast, Northern Ireland.
  Meetings: Room 315, Ashby Institute, Stranmills Road, Belfast. Fortnightly. Wednesdays, Sept.–April, 7.30 p.m.
Irish Astronomical Society
  Secretary: c/o PO Box 2547, Dublin 15, Eire.
Isle of Man Astronomical Society
  Secretary: James Martin, Ballaterson Farm, Peel, Isle of Man.
  Meetings: Quarterbridge Hotel, Douglas. 1st Thursday of each month, 8.30 p.m.
Isle of Wight Astronomical Society
  Secretary: J. W. Feakins, 1 Hilltop Cottages, High Street, Freshwater, Isle of Wight.
  Meetings: Unitarian Church Hall, Newport, Isle of Wight. Monthly.
Keele Astronomical Society
  Secretary: Miss Caterina Callus, University of Keele, Keele, Staffs.
  Meetings: As arranged during term time.
Kettering and District Astronomical Society
  Asst. Secretary: Steve Williams, 120 Brickhill Road, Wellingborough, Northants.
  Meetings: Quaker Meeting Hall, Northall Street, Kettering, Northants. 1st Tuesday each month. 7.45 p.m.
King's Lynn Amateur Astronomical Association
  Secretary: P. Twynman, 17 Poplar Avenue, RAF Marham, King's Lynn.
  Meetings: As arranged.
Lancaster and Morecambe Astronomical Society
  Secretary: Miss E. Haygarth, 27 Coulston Road, Bowerham, Lancaster.
  Meetings: Midland Hotel, Morecambe. 1st Wednesday each month except January. 7.30 p.m.
Lancaster University Astronomical Society
  Secretary: c/o Students Union, Alexandra Square, University of Lancaster.
  Meetings: As arranged.
Laymans Astronomical Society
  Secretary: John Evans, 10 Arkwright Walk, The Meadows, Nottingham.
  Meetings: The Popular, Bath Street, Ilkeston, Derbyshire. Monthly.
Leeds Astronomical Society
  Secretary: A. J. Higgins, 23 Montagu Place, Leeds LS8 2RQ.
  Meetings: Lecture Room, City Museum Library, The Headrow, Leeds.
Leicester Astronomical Society
  Secretary: Dereck Brown, 64 Grange Drive, Glen Parva, Leicester.
  Meetings: Judgemeadow Community College, Marydene Drive, Evington, Leicester. 2nd and 4th Tuesdays each month, 7.30 p.m.

Letchworth and District Astronomical Society
Secretary: Eric Hutton, 14 Folly Close, Hitchin, Herts.
Meetings: As arranged.

Limerick Astronomy Club
Secretary: Tony O'Hanlon, 26 Ballycannon Heights, Meelick, Co. Clare, Ireland.
Meetings: Limerick Senior College, Limerick, Ireland. Monthly (except June and August).
8 p.m.

Lincoln Astronomical Society
Secretary: G. Winstanley, 36 Cambridge Drive, Washingborough, Lincoln.
Meetings: The Lecture Hall, off Westcliffe Street, Lincoln. 1st Tuesday each month.

Liverpool Astronomical Society
Secretary: David Whittle, 17 Sandy Lane, Tuebrook, Liverpool.
Meetings: City Museum, Liverpool. Wednesdays and Fridays, monthly.

Loughton Astronomical Society
Meetings: Loughton Hall, Rectory Lane, Loughton, Essex. Thursdays 8 p.m.

Lowestoft and Great Yarmouth Regional Astronomers (LYRA) Society
Secretary: R. Cheek, 7 The Glades, Lowestoft, Suffolk.
Meetings: Community Wing, Kirkley High School, Kirkley Run, Lowestoft. 3rd Thursday, Sept.–
May. Afterwards in School Observatory. 7.15 p.m.

Luton & District Astronomical Society
Secretary: D. Childs, 6 Greenways, Stopsley, Luton.
Meetings: Luton College of Higher Education, Park Square, Luton. Second and last Friday each
month, 7.30 p.m.

Lytham St Annes Astronomical Association
Secretary: K. J. Porter, 141 Blackpool Road, Ansdell, Lytham St Annes, Lancs.
Meetings: College of Further Education, Clifton Drive South, Lytham St Annes. 2nd Wednesday
monthly Oct.–June.

Macclesfield Astronomical Society
Secretary: Mrs C. Moss, 27 Westminster Road, Macclesfield, Cheshire.
Meetings: The Planetarium, Jodrell Bank, 1st Tuesday each month.

Maidenhead Astronomical Society
Secretary: c/o Chairman, Peter Hunt, Hightrees, Holyport Road, Bray, Berks.
Meetings: Library. Monthly (except July) 1st Friday.

Maidstone Astronomical Society
Secretary: N. O. Harris, 19 Greenside, High Hadden, Ashford, Kent.
Meetings: Nettlestead Village Hall, 1st Tuesday in month except July and Aug. 7.30 p.m.

Manchester Astronomical Society
Secretary: J. H. Davidson, Godlee Observatory, UMIST, Sackville Street, Manchester 1.
Meetings: At the Observatory, Thursdays, 7.30–9 p.m.

Mansfield and Sutton Astronomical Society
Secretary: G. W. Shepherd, Sherwood Observatory, Coxmoor Road, Sutton-in-Ashfield, Notts.
Meetings: Sherwood Observatory, Coxmoor Road. Last Tuesday each month, 7.45 p.m.

Mexborough and Swinton Astronomical Society
Secretary: Mark R. Benton, 61 The Lea, Swinton, Mexborough, Yorks.
Meetings: Methodist Hall, Piccadilly Road, Swinton, Near Mexborough. Thursdays, 7 p.m.

Mid-Kent Astronomical Society
Secretary: Brian A. van de Peep, 11 Berber Road, Strood, Rochester, Kent.
Meetings: Medway Teachers Centre, Vicarage Road, Strood, Rochester, Kent. Last Friday in month.
Mid Kent College, Horsted. 2nd Friday in month.

Milton Keynes Astronomical Society
Secretary: The Secretary, Milton Keynes Astronomical Society, Bradwell Abbey Field Centre,
Bradwell, Milton Keynes MK1 39AP.
Meetings: Alternate Tuesdays.

Moray Astronomical Society
Secretary: Richard Pearce, 1 Forsyth Street, Hopeman, Elgin, Moray, Scotland.
Meetings: Village Hall Close, Co. Elgin.

Newbury Amateur Astronomical Society
Secretary: Mrs A. Davies, 11 Sedgfield Road, Greenham, Newbury, Berks.
Meetings: United Reform Church Hall, Cromwell Road, Newbury. Last Friday of month, Aug.–
May.

Newcastle-on-Tyne Astronomical Society
Secretary: C. E. Willits, 24 Acomb Avenue, Seaton Delaval, Tyne and Wear.
Meetings: Zoology Lecture Theatre, Newcastle University. Monthly.

North Aston Space & Astronomical Club
Secretary: W. R. Chadburn, 14 Oakdale Road, North Aston, Sheffield.
Meetings: To be notified.

Northamptonshire Natural History Astronomical Society
Secretary: Dr Nick Hewitt, 4 Daimler Close, Northampton.
Meetings: Humphrey Rooms, Castillian Terrace, Northampton. 2nd and last Monday each month.

North Devon Astronomical Society
  Secretary: P. G. Vickery, 12 Broad Park Crescent, Ilfracombe, North Devon.
  Meetings: Pilton Community College, Chaddiford Lane, Barnstaple. 1st Wednesday each month, Sept.–May.
North Dorset Astronomical Society
  Secretary: J. E. M. Coward, The Pharmacy, Stalbridge, Dorset.
  Meetings: Charterhay, Stourton, Caundle, Dorset. 2nd Wednesday each month.
North Staffordshire Astronomical Society
  Secretary: N. Oldham, 25 Linley Grove, Alsager, Stoke-on-Trent.
  Meetings: 1st Wednesday of each month at Cartwright House, Broad Street, Hanley.
North Western Association of Variable Star Observers
  Secretary: Jeremy Bullivant, 2 Beaminster Road, Heaton Mersey, Stockport, Cheshire.
  Meetings: Four annually.
Norwich Astronomical Society
  Secretary: Malcolm Jones, Tabor House, Norwich Road, Malbarton, Norwich.
  Meetings: The Observatory, Colney Lane, Colney, Norwich. Every Friday, 7.30 p.m.
Nottingham Astronomical Society
  Secretary: C. Brennan, 40 Swindon Close, Giltbrook, Nottingham.
Oldham Astronomical Society
  Secretary: P. J. Collins, 25 Park Crescent, Chadderton, Oldham.
  Meetings: Werneth Park Study Centre, Frederick Street, Oldham. Fortnightly, Friday.
Open University Astronomical Society
  Secretary: Jim Lee, c/o above, Milton Keynes.
  Meetings: Open University, Walton Hall, Milton Keynes. As arranged.
Orpington Astronomical Society
  Secretary: Miss Lucinda Jones, 263 Crescent Drive, Petts Wood, Orpington, Kent BR5 1AY.
  Meetings: Orpington Parish Church Hall, Bark Hart Road. Thursdays monthly, 7.30 p.m. Sept.–July.
Plymouth Astronomical Society
  Secretary: Sheila Evans, 40 Billington Close, Eggbuckland, Plymouth.
  Meetings: Glynnis Kingdon Centre. 2nd Friday each month.
Portsmouth Astronomical Society
  Secretary: G. B. Bryant, 81 Ringwood Road, Southsea.
  Meetings: Monday. Fortnightly.
Preston & District Astronomical Society
  Secretary: P. Sloane, 77 Ribby Road, Wrea Green, Kirkham, Preston, Lancs.
  Meetings: Moor Park (Jeremiah Horrocks) Observatory, Preston. 2nd Wednesday, last Friday each month. 7.30 p.m.
The Pulsar Group
  Secretary: Barry Smith, 157 Reridge Road, Blackburn, Lancs.
  Meetings: Amateur Astronomy Centre, Clough Bank, Bacup Road, Todmorden, Lancs. 1st Thursday each month.
Reading Astronomical Society
  Secretary: Mrs Muriel Wrigley, 516 Wokingham Road, Earley, Reading.
  Meetings: St Peter's Church Hall, Church Road, Earley. Monthly (3rd Sat.), 7 p.m.
Renfrew District Astronomical Society (formerly Paisley A.S.)
  Secretary: D. Bankhead, 3c School Wynd, Paisley.
  Meetings: Coats Observatory, Oakshaw Street, Paisley. Fridays, 7.30 p.m.
Richmond & Kew Astronomical Society
  Secretary: Emil Pallos, 10 Burleigh Place, Cambalt Road, Putney, London SW15.
  Meetings: Richmond Central Reference Library, Richmond, Surrey.
Salford Astronomical Society
  Secretary: J. A. Handford, 45 Burnside Avenue, Salford 6, Lancs.
  Meetings: The Observatory, Chaseley Road, Salford.
Salisbury Astronomical Society
  Secretary: Mrs R. Collins, Mountains, 3 Fairview Road, Salisbury, Wilts.
  Meetings: Salisbury City Library, Market Place, Salisbury.
Sandbach Astronomical Society
  Secretary: Phil Benson, 8 Gawsworth Drive, Sandbach, Cheshire.
  Meetings: Sandbach School, as arranged.
Scarborough & District Astronomical Society
  Secretary: D. M. Mainprize, 76 Trafalgar Square, Scarborough, N. Yorks.
  Meetings: Scarborough Public Library. Last Saturday each month, 7–9 p.m.
Scottish Astronomers Group
  Secretary: G. Young c/o Mills Observatory, Balgay Park, Ancrum, Dundee.
  Meetings: Bi-monthly, around the country. Syllabus given on request.
Sheffield Astronomical Society
  Secretary: Mrs Lilian M. Keen, 21 Seagrave Drive, Gleadless, Sheffield.
  Meetings: City Museum, Weston Park, 3rd Friday each month. 7.30 p.m.

Sidmouth and District Astronomical Society
Secretary: M. Grant, Salters Meadow, Sidmouth, Devon.
Meetings: Norman Lockyer Observatory, Salcombe Hill. 1st Monday in each month.

Solent Amateur Astronomers
Secretary: R. Smith, 16 Lincoln Close, Woodley, Romsey, Hants.
Meetings: Room 2, Oaklands Community Centre, Fairisle Road, Lordshill, Southampton. 3rd Tuesday.

Southampton Astronomical Society
Secretary: C. R. Braines, 1a Drummond Road, Hythe, Southampton.
Meetings: Room 148, Murray Building, Southampton University, 2nd Thursday each month, 7.30 p.m.

South Astronomical Society
Secretary: G. T. Elston, 34 Plummer Road, Clapham Park, London SW4 8HH.

South Downs Astronomical Society
Secretary: J. Green, 46 Central Avenue, Bognor Regis, West Sussex.
Meetings: Assembly Rooms, Chichester. 1st Friday in each month.

South-East Essex Astronomical Society
Secretary: C. Jones, 92 Long Riding, Basildon, Essex.
Meetings: Lecture Theatre, Central Library, Victoria Avenue, Southend-on-Sea. Generally 1st Thursday in month, Sept.–May.

South-East Kent Astronomical Society
Secretary: P. Andrew, 7 Farncombe Way, Whitfield, nr. Dover.
Meetings: Monthly.

South Lincolnshire Astronomical & Geophysical Society
Secretary: Ian Farley, 12 West Road, Bourne, Lincs.
Meetings: South Holland Centre, Spalding. 3rd Thursday each month, Sept.–May. 7.30 p.m.

South London Astronomical Society
Chairman: P. Bruce, 2 Constance Road, West Croydon CR0 2RS.
Meetings: Surrey Halls, Birfield Road, Stockwell, London SW4. 2nd Tuesday each month, 8 p.m.

Southport Astronomical Society
Secretary: R. Rawlinson, 188 Haig Avenue, Southport, Merseyside.
Meetings: Monthly Sept.–May, plus observing sessions.

Southport, Ormskirk and District Astronomical Society
Secretary: J. T. Harrison, 92 Cottage Lane, Ormskirk, Lancs L39 3NJ.
Meetings: Saturday evenings, monthly as arranged.

South Shields Astronomical Society
Secretary: c/o South Tyneside College, St George's Avenue, South Shields.
Meetings: Marine and Technical College. Each Thursday, 7.30 p.m.

South Somerset Astronomical Society
Secretary: G. McNelly, 11 Laxton Close, Taunton, Somerset.
Meetings: Victoria Inn, Skittle Alley, East Reach, Taunton. Last Saturday each month, 7.30 p.m.

South-West Cotswolds Astronomical Society
Secretary: C. R. Wiles, Old Castle House, The Triangle, Malmesbury, Wilts.
Meetings: 2nd Friday each month, 8 p.m. (Sept.–June).

South-West Herts Astronomical Society
Secretary: Frank Phillips, 54 Highfield Way, Rickmansworth, Herts.
Meetings: Rickmansworth. Last Friday each month, Sept.–May.

Stafford and District Astronomical Society
Secretary: Mrs L. Hodkinson, Beecholme, Francis Green Lane, Penkridge, Staffs.
Meetings: Riverside Centre, Stafford. Every 3rd Thursday, Sept.–May, 7.30 p.m.

Stirling Astronomical Society
Secretary: R. H. Lynn, 25 Pullar Avenue, Bridge of Allan, Stirling.
Meetings: Smith Museum & Art Gallery, Dumbarton Road, Stirling. 2nd Friday each month, 7.30 p.m.

Stoke-on-Trent Astronomical Society
Secretary: M. Pace, Sundale, Dunnocksfold Road, Alsager, Stoke-on-Trent.
Meetings: Cartwright House, Broad Street, Hanley. Monthly.

Sussex Astronomical Society
Secretary: Mrs C. G. Sutton, 75 Vale Road, Portslade, Sussex.
Meetings: English Language Centre, Third Avenue, Hove. Every Wednesday, 7.30–9.30 p.m. Sept.–May.

Swansea Astronomical Society
Secretary: D. F. Tovey, 43 Cecil Road, Gowerton, Swansea.
Meetings: Dillwyn Llewellyn School, John Street, Cockett, Swansea. Second and fourth Thursday each month at 7.30 p.m.

Tavistock Astronomical Society
Secretary: D. S. Gibbs, Lanherne, Chollacott Lane, Whitchurch, Tavistock, Devon.
Meetings: Science Laboratory, Kelly College, Tavistock. 1st Wednesday in month. 7.30 p.m.

Thames Valley Astronomical Group
 Secretary: K. J. Pallet, 82a Tennyson Street, South Lambeth, London SW8 3TH.
 Meetings: Irregular.
Thanet Amateur Astronomical Society
 Secretary: P. F. Jordan, 85 Crescent Road, Ramsgate.
 Meetings: Hilderstone House, Broadstairs, Kent. Monthly.
Torbay Astronomical Society
 Secretary: R. Jones, St Helens, Hermose Road, Teignmouth, Devon.
 Meetings: Town Hall, Torquay. 3rd Thursday, Oct.–May.
Tullamore Astronomical Society
 Secretary: S. McKenna, 145 Arden Vale, Tullamore, Co. Offaly, Eire.
 Meetings: Tullamore Vocational School, Fortnightly, Tuesdays, Oct–June. 8 p.m.
Usk Astronomical Society
 Secretary: D. J. T. Thomas, 20 Maryport Street, Usk, Gwent.
 Meetings: Usk Adult Education Centre, Maryport Street. Weekly, Thursdays (term dates).
Vectis Astronomical Society
 Secretary: J. W. Smith, 27 Forest Road, Winford, Sandown, I.W.
 Meetings: 4th Friday each month, except Dec. at Lord Louis Library Meeting Room, Newport, I.W.
Webb Society
 Secretary: S. J. Hynes, 8 Cormorant Close, Sydney, Crewe, Cheshire.
 Meetings: As arranged.
Wellingborough District Astronomical Society
 Secretary: S. M. Williams, 120 Brickhill Road, Wellingborough, Northants.
 Meetings: On 2nd Wednesday. Gloucester Hall, Church Street, Wellingborough, 7.30 p.m.
Wessex Astronomical Society
 Secretary: Leslie Fry, 14 Hanhum Road, Corfe Mullen, Dorset.
 Meetings: Allendale Centre, Wimborne, Dorset. 1st Tuesday of each month.
West of London Astronomical Society
 Secretary: A. H. Davis, 49 Beaulieu Drive, Pinner, Middlesex HA5 1NB.
 Meetings: Monthly, alternately at Hillingdon and North Harrow. 2nd Monday of the month, except August.
West Midlands Astronomical Association
 Secretary: Miss S. Bundy, 93 Greenridge Road, Handsworth Wood, Birmingham.
 Meetings: Dr Johnson House, Bull Street, Birmingham. As arranged.
West Yorkshire Astronomical Society
 Secretary: K. Willoughby, 11 Hardisty Drive, Pontefract, Yorks.
 Meetings: Rosse Observatory, Carleton Community Centre, Carleton Road, Pontefract, each Tuesday, 7.15 to 9 p.m.
Whittington Astronomical Society
 Secretary: Peter Williamson, The Observatory, Top Street, Whittington, Shropshire.
 Meetings: The Observatory every month.
Wolverhampton Astronomical Society
 Secretary: M. Astley, Garwick, 8 Holme Mill, Fordhouses, Wolverhampton.
 Meetings: Beckminster Methodist Church Hall, Birches Road, Wolverhampton. Alternate Mondays, Sept.–April.
Worcester Astronomical Society
 Secretary: Arthur Wilkinson, 179 Henwick Road, St Johns, Worcester.
 Meetings: Room 117, Worcester College of Higher Education, Henwick Grove, Worcester. 2nd Thursday each month.
Worthing Astronomical Society
 Contact: G. Boots, 101 Ardingly Drive, Worthing, Sussex.
 Meetings: Adult Education Centre, Union Place, Worthing, Sussex. 1st Wednesday each month (except August). 7.30 p.m.
Wycombe Astronomical Society
 Secretary: P. A. Hodgins, 50 Copners Drive, Holmer Green, High Wycombe, Bucks.
 Meetings: 3rd Wednesday each month, 7.45 p.m.
York Astronomical Society
 Secretary: Simon Howard, 20 Manor Drive South, Acomb, York.
 Meetings: Goddricke College, York University. 1st and 3rd Fridays.

Any society wishing to be included in this list of local societies or to update details are invited to write to the Editor (c/o Messrs Sidgwick & Jackson (Publishers), Ltd, Cavaye Place, London SW10 9PG), so that the relevant information may be included in the next edition of the *Yearbook*.